POCAHONTAS, *Seymour*
SACAGAWEA, *Seymour*
SEQUOYAH, *Snow*
SITTING BULL, *Stevenson*
SQUANTO, *Stevenson*
TECUMSEH, *Stevenson*

NAVAL HEROES

DAVID FARRAGUT, *Long*
GEORGE DEWEY, *Long*
JOHN PAUL JONES, *Snow*
MATTHEW CALBRAITH PERRY, *Scharbach*
OLIVER HAZARD PERRY, *Long*
RAPHAEL SEMMES, *Snow*
STEPHEN DECATUR, *Smith*

NOTED WIVES and MOTHERS

ABIGAIL ADAMS, *Wagoner*
DOLLY MADISON, *Monsell*
JESSIE FREMONT, *Wagoner*
MARTHA WASHINGTON, *Wagoner*
MARY TODD LINCOLN, *Wilkie*
NANCY HANKS, *Stevenson*
RACHEL JACKSON, *Govan*

SCIENTISTS and INVENTORS

ALBERT EINSTEIN, *Hammontree*
ALECK BELL, *Widdemer*
CYRUS MCCORMICK, *Dobler*
ELI WHITNEY, *Snow*
ELIAS HOWE, *Corcoran*
ELIZABETH BLACKWELL, *Henry*
GEORGE CARVER, *Stevenson*
GEORGE EASTMAN, *Henry*
HENRY FORD, *Aird and Ruddiman*
JOHN AUDUBON, *Mason*
LUTHER BURBANK, *Burt*
MARIA MITCHELL, *Melin*
ROBERT FULTON, *Henry*
SAMUEL MORSE, *Snow*
TOM EDISON, *Guthridge*
WALTER REED, *Higgins*
WILBUR AND ORVILLE WRIGHT, *Stevenson*
WILL AND CHARLIE MAYO, *Hammontree*

BETSY ROSS, *Weil*
BOOKER T. WASHINGTON, *Stevenson*
CLARA BARTON, *Stevenson*
DAN BEARD, *Mason*
FRANCES WILLARD, *Mason*
JANE ADDAMS, *Wagoner*
J. STERLING MORTON, *Moore*
JULIA WARD HOWE, *Wagoner*
JULIETTE LOW, *Higgins*
LILIUOKALANI, *Newman*
LUCRETIA MOTT, *Burnett*
MOLLY PITCHER, *Stevenson*
OLIVER WENDELL HOLMES, JR., *Dunham*
SUSAN ANTHONY, *Monsell*

SOLDIERS

ANTHONY WAYNE, *Stevenson*
BEDFORD FORREST, *Parks*
DAN MORGAN, *Bryant*
ETHAN ALLEN, *Winders*
FRANCIS MARION, *Steele*
ISRAEL PUTNAM, *Stevenson*
JEB STUART, *Winders*
NATHANAEL GREENE, *Peckham*
ROBERT E. LEE, *Monsell*
SAM HOUSTON, *Stevenson*
TOM JACKSON, *Monsell*
U. S. GRANT, *Stevenson*
WILLIAM HENRY HARRISON, *Peckham*
ZACK TAYLOR, *Wilkie*

STATESMEN

ABE LINCOLN, *Stevenson*
ANDY JACKSON, *Stevenson*
DAN WEBSTER, *Smith*
FRANKLIN ROOSEVELT, *Weil*
HENRY CLAY, *Monsell*
JAMES MONROE, *Widdemer*
JEFF DAVIS, *de Grummond and Delaune*
JOHN MARSHALL, *Monsell*
TEDDY ROOSEVELT, *Parks*
WOODROW WILSON, *Monsell*

Babe Didrikson

Girl Athlete

Illustrated by James Ponter

Babe Didrikson

Girl Athlete

By Lena Young de Grummond and
Lynn de Grummond Delaune

THE **BOBBS-MERRILL** COMPANY, INC.
A SUBSIDIARY OF HOWARD W. SAMS & CO., INC.
Publishers • INDIANAPOLIS • NEW YORK

LIBRARY OF CONGRESS CATALOG CARD NUMBER: 63-10310

This book is
dedicated
to
our good friend,
J. W. "Red" Irvine

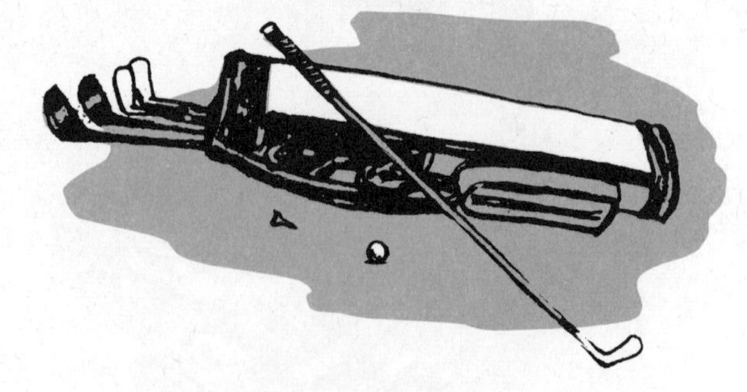

Illustrations

Full pages

Numerous smaller illustrations

Contents

★ ★ ★

Books by Lena Young de Grummond and Lynn de Grummond Delaune

JEFF DAVIS: CONFEDERATE BOY

★ ★ # Babe Didrikson

Girl Athlete

Little Whirlwind and Big Storm

"THREE POUNDS of rice! Five pounds of sugar!" Mr. Mamaschella looked up. He went to the door of the little neighborhood grocery store.

"That's Babe calling, Mamma," he said. His plump wife stood behind the store counter. "Do we have three pounds of rice already measured? I did up some five pound packages of sugar this morning." At that time stores kept many things in huge barrels. Almost everything had to be weighed or measured for each customer.

"I'll hurry and do up the three pounds," said Mrs. Mamaschella. She poured the rice into a bag on the scale. "That Babe!" she said, smiling.

"Calling her order on the way so it will be all ready by the time she gets here."

Just then a small blue-eyed whirlwind burst into the shop. The whirlwind, in the person of a wiry little girl, was wearing blue jeans and her brother's shirt. She raced toward the counter. She plunked down her money and grabbed the packages. Mrs. Mamaschella had them all ready.

"Trying to better your record, Babe?" asked Mr. Mamaschella. "I'm sure you can already come to the store faster than anyone else in your family."

"Yes, sir," said Babe. She was already scooting out the door. "But I want to be able to do it faster than anybody else in the whole neighborhood." Away she raced.

"How about in all of Beaumont?" Mr. Mamaschella called after her teasingly. "Or maybe in the whole state of Texas?"

"Don't suggest it—she'll try it," said Mrs.

Mamaschella, laughing. She joined her husband at the door. Together they watched the small figure tearing down the sidewalk. "That Babe," said Mrs. Mamaschella, fondly. "She always wants to do things better than everybody else."

"She will, too," said Mr. Mamaschella, "working at it the way she does."

Babe ran down Doucette Street. She went racing up the front steps of the frame house where the Didriksons lived. She rushed into the kitchen, panting.

Her mother turned from the table where she was making meatballs. "My goodness, Babe," she said, "back already? I didn't think you'd even be *at* the store yet, much less *back!*"

Babe beamed with pride. "I did go pretty fast, didn't I, Momma?" she asked. She put the packages of rice and sugar away. "Now may I go out and play?"

"Yes, my girl," said Mrs. Didrikson. She gave

the shiny brown hair an affectionate pat. "But don't forget to come home in time to set the table. It's your turn."

"Yes, ma'am," answered Babe. She was already halfway out of the room.

A few minutes later she was running down the block. A group of neighborhood boys saw her coming. They were choosing sides for a game of baseball.

"Hey, here's Mildred Didrikson," said one.

The little girl turned on him. "You take that back!" she said. She started to pound on him with her fists.

"Hey—hey!" he said. He backed away. He knew those fists were as hard as any boy's. "I was just teasing! Mildred's your name, isn't it?"

"Yes, but nobody better call me that, you hear?" She doubled her fists again.

"Okay, Babe, okay," said the boy. He grinned. "I'm sorry."

"Well, that's all right," she said. She was all smiles now. She looked around. "You all getting ready to start a game? Can I play?"

"Sure thing," said the boy. He turned to the others. "Hey, we choose Babe for our side!"

"No, you don't," said another. "We want her!"

"We said so first!"

"Well, all right. But we get her next time! Babe may be little, but she's one of the best players in the neighborhood."

Babe thought she had been playing only a few minutes when she heard a familiar call. "Babe! Babe! Momma says you come home right now! Everybody's waiting for you so we can eat supper." It was her sister Lillie.

"Aw, Babe, do you have to go?" asked one of her teammates.

"I sure do," said Babe. "When Momma says come home, she means just that. I'll come again tomorrow." She hurried off to join her sister.

"Babe, it was your turn to set the table," said Lillie accusingly. "I had to do it."

"Gee, Lillie, I'm sorry," said Babe. She gave her big sister a hug. "I'll do it two times straight."

Lillie smiled. She never could stay mad at Babe long. She was only two years older than Babe. The two girls were very close.

When the two little girls came into the dining room, the others were already at the table. There were Dora and Esther Nancy, Babe's two oldest sisters. There was her oldest brother, young Ole. The Didriksons pronounced his name the Norwegian way, "Oley." There was Lillie's twin, Louis. There was the youngest of the big family, Arthur or "Bubba."

Poppa sat at he head of the long table. Babe and Lillie hurriedly slipped into their seats. They had got there just in time. Momma was just coming in with a big bowl of steaming meatballs. In a few minutes everyone was eating.

The instant supper was finished, Babe jumped up. She started clearing the table quickly.

"My goodness, Babe," said her mother, "not so fast! There won't be any dishes left to wash at that rate."

"Then we would get through awful fast, Momma," said Babe, grinning.

Momma laughed. "Well, that's a short cut we don't need, young lady! Now, let's see—it's your turn to wash and Lillie's to dry."

"Yes, ma'am," said Babe. "Come on, Lillie, let's hurry." In a few minutes the sounds of water splashing and dishes clattering could be heard from the kitchen.

Mrs. Didrikson sat down in the big rocking chair. She picked up her darning basket. Mr. Didrikson was sitting nearby, smoking his pipe.

"Just listen to that noise, Ole," said Mrs. Didrikson. "I declare, it's a wonder the dishes survive when it's Babe's turn to wash them."

Mr. Didrikson smiled. "Yes," he said. "Whatever she does, she does with all her might."

It wasn't long before Babe came running into the dining room. "All finished, Momma!"

Momma looked up from her darning. "Good," she said.

"Do we have any dishes left?" asked Poppa. He was smiling.

"Now, Poppa," said Babe, grinning back at him. "You know I'm just about the best dishwasher in the whole world!"

Poppa laughed. Babe climbed up on his lap. She gave him a hug. "Tell us a story, Poppa."

"Oh, yes, Poppa, please do," begged Lillie. She came over to sit at his feet. In a minute Louis and Arthur were there, too.

Poppa had gone to sea from Norway when he was very young. He had made many sailing voyages. He had gone around Cape Horn almost twenty times.

"Tell us about the time you and the others got shipwrecked on an island and had to eat monkeys and all sorts of things," said Babe.

"I just told that one the other night," said Poppa. He patted her head. "Now let's see—suppose I tell you about the storm at Cape Horn."

Babe turned on his lap so she could watch his face. Her eyes were shining. She loved Poppa's stories.

"The weather had been good—unusually good—for the whole first part of the voyage," Poppa began. "We were getting close to the Horn, though, so we knew it couldn't hold.

"There was an old sailor on board—Hansen, his name was. He looked like a regular pirate. He'd lost an eye somewhere or other and wore a black patch over it. He even had a parrot that liked to sit on his shoulder!

"Well, he kept telling us that the could *feel* it—something terrible was going to happen! He'd come out on deck and look around, scowling up at the sky with that one eye and shaking his head.

" 'Ah—it'll be dreadful,' he'd say softly, 'dreadful!' and he'd kind of shudder. Here it was—a beautiful day and all, and he'd say that. It was enough to make the hair rise on the back of your neck." Babe could almost feel her hair rise as she listened.

Her father went on. "Well, sure enough, just as we were starting to round the Horn, the storm struck! And how it struck! I've seen many a storm in my time, but this was the monster of them all!"

"It was really a bad one, wasn't it, Poppa?" said Babe. She snuggled closer.

"I'll say it was," said Mr. Didrikson. "It picked up our ship and threw it from wave to wave like a man throwing a baseball from one hand to the other. Everything on that ship crashed and slid.

"Some barrels came unlashed and rolled across the decks like cannonballs. Men were running everywhere trying to keep from being hit.

"Then somebody came flying up from below. 'The ship!' he shouted. 'It's starting to go to pieces!'

" 'Old Hansen,' we all thought. 'It's just like old Hansen said!' The hair *really* stood up on the backs of our necks then, I can tell you!"

"Oh, Poppa!" said Babe. "What did you do?" She felt as if she were right there in the storm with him.

"The ship started shivering and creaking," said Poppa. "You could just feel her coming apart beneath you! Then almost before you knew it there was water everywhere.

"A heavy wave came crashing across what had been a solid deck a few minutes before—now it was breaking up before our very eyes! I was thrown head first into the water.

"I went down for what seemed hours. I came up choking and grabbed the first thing that came to hand. It turned out to be a rope fastened to a mast.

"There were pieces of the ship floating all around. Men were shouting and struggling in the water. It was dreadful—as dreadful as old Hansen had said it would be!

"Suddenly I heard a weak voice near me. Someone was calling 'Ole—Ole!' I turned. There was old Hansen. He was struggling in the water near me.

"I saw him just as he was slipping under the water. 'Here, Hansen, here!' I cried. I leaned over as far as I could. I grabbed one of his arms and pulled him up. 'Thanks,' he gasped weakly.

"From then on it was up to me. I held on to Hansen with one hand and to the mast rope with another. The storm tossed us around for ages.

"Sometimes my arms got so tired I thought they would come off, but I held on anyway. My grip on that mast rope was all that lay between us and certain death.

"At last the sea calmed down. Rescue boats finally arrived. Nothing I'd ever seen looked so wonderful as those boats! When we were hauled aboard, we had been in the water four hours. I was a tired but happy sailor that night!"

"How about old Hansen?" asked Babe.

"He was fine," said Poppa. "Kept telling everybody how I'd saved his life and all. And now," he said, "it's bedtime." He put Babe down.

"Oh, Poppa, can't you tell us another one?" asked Babe.

"Please, Poppa," begged Lillie and Louis.

"Not tonight," said Poppa. "It's bedtime. Off you go." He gave each of them a hug and kiss.

A little later Babe and Lillie were lying in bed. They were thinking about the story. Lillie said wistfully, "Someday I hope something exciting happens to me like the things that have happened to Poppa."

"I'm going to have exciting things happen to me," said Babe firmly.

"How do you know?" asked Lillie.

"I'll *make* them happen!" was the answer.

The Marble Contest

THE NEXT morning Babe was up and dressed earlier than usual. She ran into the dining room. "Good morning, Momma," she said, giving her mother a hug.

She bounced into her chair at the table. "May I start now?" she asked. "I'm hungry as a bear this morning."

Momma smiled. "You're always hungry as a bear," she said. "Wait just a minute. Here come Lillie and Louis and Bubba. You all may start now. Dora, Esther Nancy, and young Ole ate earlier."

There was a saucer on top of each bowl of

oatmeal on the table. Babe took the saucer off and looked into her bowl. "Butter's all melted," she said happily. She ate a big spoonful.

"Poppa surely does fix good oatmeal."

Every morning before he went to work Poppa made oatmeal for the whole family. He spooned it into the bowls, put butter and sugar on top, and then put a saucer over each bowl. When the children came down to breakfast the oatmeal was ready and waiting.

In a few minutes Babe was finished. She jumped up and started toward the door.

"Babe!" her mother called.

Babe stopped. "Yes, ma'am?" she answered.

"You can't go out to play until you've done your chores."

"Oh, Momma, can't I please go now? I've got to go to school extra early this morning."

Mrs. Didrikson came out of the kitchen wiping her hands. "Why?" she asked.

"Because there's a marble contest today. I want to get in a little practice before there are too many kids on the school ground," said Babe.

"Then hurry and get your chores done extra fast. No skipping out before you're through either, young lady," said Momma firmly.

"Yes, ma'am," said Babe. She hurried off to do her tasks. Every one of the Didrikson children had to help with a certain part of the work.

Soon Babe was finished and on her way to Magnolia Elementary School. When Lillie got there a little later, she found Babe already hard at play with a group of little boys.

"Babe!" she called.

Babe looked up.

"Come here just a minute," said Lillie.

Babe left the marble players and came over.

"You told Momma you were going to enter the school marble contest. Are you really going to? Louis says it's for boys."

"They said I could enter," said Babe. "I asked my teacher. She said she guessed anybody in the whole school could enter if he wanted to. Maybe mostly boys will enter, but girls can."

"Well, besides that, it's for all the grades," said Lillie. "There'll be big boys from the sixth grade and everything. And you're just in the second grade. I don't think you ought to enter."

"It's all right, Lillie," said Babe. "You don't need to worry. I'll do all right."

"I'm still not sure," said Lillie slowly. Just then the school bell rang.

"See you later!" called Babe. She ran off to get in line.

Later that morning Lillie's teacher made an announcement. "All boys entering the marble tournament will report to Mr. Parker on the playground behind the school. The finals will be held during the noon recess so that everyone can watch."

"Well," thought Lillie, "I hope Babe has decided not to try. She's a good marble shooter, but she'd look silly, a little second-grade girl with all those big boys. Of course once Babe makes up her mind——"

Lillie began her lessons. Soon she had completely forgotten about the marble tournament. When noon came she was eating her lunch as usual. She was just taking her second sandwich out of the bag when Louis came running up. He was excited.

"Hey, Lillie!" he yelled. "Babe's in the finals of the marble tournament. Let's go watch!"

Lillie jumped to her feet. Lunch was forgotten. She ran to catch up with her twin brother. In a few minutes they had reached the tournament area. They pushed their way through the children crowded around the marble players.

"See—there she is," said Louis. A small figure crouched near the edge of the big marble ring.

It was Babe. She looked especially little next to the other marble players. She was the only girl. She was much younger than any of the other children who were left in the contest.

Mr. Parker was in charge of the tournament. "We're down to the finals now," he said. "We have two players left. One is a boy from the sixth grade. The other," he added with a smile, "is the one girl to enter the contest, a second-grader, Mildred Didrikson.

"The first player to knock seven marbles out of the ring will win the game. The winner of the tournament must win two out of three games. The players will lag to see who shoots first."

Babe and Mike lagged. Mike's shooter stopped closer to the line. "Mike gets to shoot first," said Mr. Parker. Babe crouched down to watch.

Mike knuckled down. One marble after the other went out of the ring. Soon Mike had shot out five marbles.

"Golly," thought Babe, "I hope I at least get a chance to shoot."

Mike shot again and missed. Babe breathed a sigh of relief.

"All right, Babe, your turn," said Mr. Parker. Babe knuckled down to shoot. Out went one marble, then another. Then she missed.

"I told her she shouldn't enter," whispered Lillie to Louis.

Mike easily shot two marbles out of the ring. The children watching the game clapped. "One game for Mike, 7-2," announced Mr. Parker.

Babe and Mike lagged again. This time Babe got to shoot first. She went down. She started shooting. Five marbles went out, one after the other. Then she missed.

Mike took his turn. One by one he got six marbles out. "Only one more," thought Babe. She watched Mike knuckle down. He shot—and missed!

Hurriedly Babe crouched down. She knocked one marble out—and then another.

"Hooray!" shouted Lillie and Louis together.

"At least she's won one game," said Lillie.

"One game for Babe, 7-6," announced Mr. Parker. "This next game will decide the tournament. Lag to see who shoots first."

Once more Mike won the lag. He shot one marble out. He shot out another. Then he missed.

"Now's my chance," thought Babe. She shot carefully and steadily. And out went the marbles—one, two, three, four, five, six, seven! The boys and girls watching shouted.

"Babe wins the tournament!" said Mr. Parker.

Walking home from school that afternoon, Babe heard someone call. She stopped and turned around. Lillie was running to catch up with her.

"Hi, Lillie," she said. "I won the tournament."

"I know," said Lillie. "I saw you. I thought you did real well."

Babe beamed.

Lillie went on, "I've decided I'm not going to waste my time worrying about you in tournaments any more."

"I think that's a good idea, Lillie," said Babe. "I believe I can pretty well take care of myself in tournaments from now on."

A Trip to the Circus

"BABE! BABE!" Mrs. Didrikson opened the front door just as her youngest daughter was running out of the yard.

Babe stopped. "What is it, Momma?"

"Did you finish the scrubbing? I was looking out the kitchen window and saw you leaving. I wanted to make sure you were through before you left."

"I finished, Momma," said Babe.

"Well, come back and we'll go and look at it," said Mrs. Didrikson.

"I hurried up so I could go over to see Christine's Aunt Minnie. The circus will be here tomorrow. Christine said her Aunt Minnie has invited us to go with her."

"Is this the circus Minnie used to work with?" asked Mrs. Didrikson. She and Babe were walking back toward the girls' bedroom.

"Yes, Momma," was the reply. "Christine says Aunt Minnie used to hang by her teeth way up at the top of the tent, miles above the ground. Then she'd turn around and around. She went so fast she was just a blur. Then at the end, she'd slide all the way down—250 feet, Christine says—still hanging by her teeth! I'd love to try that!"

Momma laughed. "You would, too!" she said. She gently mussed the little girl's hair. "Ah, Babe," she said, "you're such a daredevil!"

They walked out onto the big sleeping porch. Mr. Didrikson had added it to the main house as the family grew and they needed more bedrooms. It was divided into two parts. The boys slept in one part. The girls slept in the other.

Each room was large. There were twenty-eight windows on the whole porch! Babe was supposed to have scrubbed the floor in the girls' room.

"Well, Babe," said Mrs. Didrikson. "I'm glad to see that it *has* been scrubbed." She walked around looking carefully at the linoleum floor. "It's a pretty good job except for this part. You must have hurried here."

"Yes, ma'am, I guess I did," admitted Babe. "I was trying to get through so I could go to see Aunt Minnie."

"Well, you just start right in and do this part over again—and no streaks now, young lady. Then you can go over and see Minnie." Momma went back to the kitchen.

Babe grabbed the bucket. Quickly she filled it with suds. She tied a scrub brush to each foot. In a few minutes she was skating rapidly over the floor, scrubbing as she went.

"There!" she said. She gave a final quick skate. She pulled off the brushes. She picked up all the cleaning equipment and put it away. Then once more she was on her way to Aunt Minnie's.

"Hello, Babe," said Aunt Minnie, letting her in the front door. "I was just telling Christine that we'll leave about an hour and a half before the circus starts tomorrow night."

"We should be able to get extra good seats that early," said Babe.

"Oh, we don't have to worry about seats," said Aunt Minnie. "The circus always saves some special seats for me and my guests." She smiled proudly. "We're going early so we can visit everyone before the show starts."

"Boy, that'll be wonderful!" said Babe. "I'll be ready in plenty of time."

"Good," said Aunt Minnie.

Babe always enjoyed school, but she found the next day long. She kept thinking about the circus.

At last school was over, and Babe raced home. In no time at all she was busy with her chores. Mrs. Didrikson had a friend, Mrs. Hansen from Port Arthur, visiting her.

"My goodness," said Mrs. Hansen. "Babe certainly is working hard today!"

Mrs. Didrikson laughed. "Yes," she said. "This is one time I didn't have to remind her. It's because of the circus tonight. She knows she can't go until she finishes her chores."

It wasn't long before Babe was finished. Lillie and Louis had been busy, too. Soon they and Bubba, the youngest of the family, were all dressed and ready to go. They kissed Momma and Poppa good-by.

"Have a good time!" said Poppa.

"We will!" called Babe. The four children ran across the yard.

Soon they, Christine, and Aunt Minnie were on their way to the circus. In just a little while they reached the field where the circus was being held.

"Oh, look," cried Babe. "There's the tent!" Even though it was not time for the circus to start, the huge tent was already a busy place. Men and women hurried to and fro. Some of them were already in costume.

Aunt Minnie and the group of children walked up to the entrance. Babe fairly danced with excitement. A clown was standing nearby. He looked up as they drew closer. Then he hurried over to them, smiling.

"Well, Minnie!" he said, holding out his hand. "It's good to see you." He and Aunt Minnie shook hands. He looked at the five children. "Don't tell me all these are yours?" he asked.

Aunt Minnie laughed. "No, I'm afraid not. This is my niece, Christine McCandless. The others are neighborhood children." She introduced Babe and her sister and brothers to him.

Very seriously he shook hands with each one of them. Just as he started to shake Babe's hand, he said, "My goodness, this little girl has something behind her ear. Let's see what it is. Well, imagine that—it's a duck!"

Reaching behind Babe's ear, he pulled out a tiny yellow duckling! It started to quack at once. Everybody laughed.

"Oh, please let me hold it," said Babe. The clown put the soft, fluffy little ball of down into her hands. She held it gently. The others crowded around to pet it. Aunt Minnie talked to the clown, whose name turned out to be Joe.

"I have to go now," said Joe a few minutes later. "May I have Alphonso back?" he asked.

Carefully Babe handed him the little duckling. "Good-by, Alphonso," she said.

"Good-by," said the clown. He waved his hand in front of Alphonso. The little duckling disappeared. The children were delighted.

"How did he do that?" asked Babe.

"He's very good at sleight-of-hand," said Aunt Minnie. "Joe always uses little tricks like that in his act. You'll probably see some more later. Come on now. Let's go. We want to look around before it's time to go to our seats."

Babe and the others followed Aunt Minnie from one little red dressing-room to another. They met acrobats, wild animal trainers, the fat lady, and the thin man. They watched the clowns make up.

Babe looked at some of them putting on their white paint and big red noses. "I love watching ordinary people turn into clowns right before your very eyes," she said to Lillie.

Then something else caught her attention. "Look at that," she said. She pointed to a clown putting on long, long stilts. When he stood up he was fifteen feet tall! "Boy, would I like to walk on those!" she said.

"You couldn't," said Lillie. "You'd fall."

"Oh, I might at first," answered Babe, "but I bet it wouldn't take me long to learn how. Then could I get places in a hurry! I could make it to Mamaschella's in about three steps!"

Just then Aunt Minnie called them. "I just saw the band go in. The show will start soon now. We'd better go to our seats." Aunt Minnie led the way into the huge tent.

She stopped at the first row of reserved seats.

"Golly, Aunt Minnie," said Babe. "Are we going to be able to sit on the very first row?"

"Yes, we are," said Aunt Minnie. "We're just in time, too. The show's starting right now."

Babe thought the next few hours passed like minutes. Many things were going on at once, and it was interesting to see all the people she had met earlier doing their acts.

Lillie shrank back when the elephants went by. "They're so *close*," she whispered to Babe.

"I love it!" said Babe. "I'd like to reach right out and touch them." She turned toward the ring entrance. "Oh, here come the clowns!"

The line of clowns moved into the tent. "There's the clown with the stilts!" cried Babe excitedly. She stood up and waved. "Look, he sees us! He's waving back!"

The parade of clowns continued. Babe laughed with delight when a little pig came by. "Look," she said, "he's got on a clown's hat and ruffles around his neck and everything!"

Then she saw Joe. He was just pulling an old shoe from behind another clown's ear. Everyone laughed and laughed.

Next Joe went up on the front row. He picked up a man's hat and pulled a big white bunny out of it. In a few minutes he was directly in front of Aunt Minnie and her guests.

He looked up and saw Babe. She grinned down at him.

"Aha," he said. "There's the little girl who has ducks behind her ears!" He ran up to their seats. "Hello," he said, "do you have any more ducks behind your ears?"

Babe grinned. "I don't think so," she said. "I think I only had one."

"Only one, huh?" said the clown. He reached behind Babe's ear. Out came a little yellow duckling.

Babe laughed. "Maybe two," she said.

"Two, huh?" said Joe. Quickly he reached behind her ear again and again. He brought out one, two, three, four more little yellow ducklings! How the crowd clapped and laughed! Babe clapped and laughed with them. She was having a wonderful time.

The acrobats and tight-rope artists came next. Babe loved to watch them fly from one swing to another. How exciting it was to watch them balance on that narrow wire so high above the audience!

"I bet that's really fun," she thought.

At last the show was over. Soon Aunt Minnie and her little group were back on Doucette Street. The four Didrikson children thanked Aunt Minnie for their exciting evening. "It was swell," said Babe. "I think I'll be an acrobat in a circus when I grow up!"

Aunt Millie laughed. She gave Babe a little

hug. "I don't doubt but what you could!" she said. "I don't doubt it at all."

The Didricksons ran to their house. Babe dashed breathlessly inside. "We had a grand time, Momma!" she cried. "There were acrobats who did all sorts of things. I'm going to try them tomorrow! And guess what—I had six ducks behind my ears!"

"The Flying Didriksons!"

Babe was as good as her word. Bright and early the next morning she was out in the yard. She was ready to start being an acrobat.

In a little while she came bouncing into the kitchen. "Momma," she said, "can I have that old rope Poppa has in the shed? It's been there for ages. I don't think he's going to use it."

Mrs. Didrikson looked up. She was making fishcakes. "Rope?" she said. "Oh, yes, I remember. I heard Poppa say he didn't need it. What do you want it for?"

"We're going to make swings," said Babe. Her eyes glowed. "We're going to make trapezes like they have in the circus. May we have it, Momma? May we?"

"Well, all right," said Mrs. Didrikson. "Only be careful. And don't go climbing up on any housetops, either."

Babe grinned. Her mother had seen her playing follow the leader a few weeks earlier. Babe had been the leader. She had climbed right up to the top of a new house which was being built. She had been walking along the very highest part of the roof. Then she had missed her step.

"I won't, Momma," said Babe. "We're just going to climb around in the old chinaberry tree in the backyard."

Babe got the rope. She rounded up Lillie, Louis, and Bubba. The four of them set to work on the swings.

"What are we going to use for seats, Babe?" asked Louis. "You know Poppa's not going to let us cut up any of his good lumber."

"I know," said Babe. "But I've got three old broom handles. I got Momma to give them to me last week. I figured they'd come in handy for something. You remember the acrobats in the circus. Their swings had bars instead of flat boards for seats."

"Say, that's right," said Louis. "Well, you get them and I'll saw them."

Soon the trapezes were made. Babe climbed up the big chinaberry tree. "Throw the ropes up, Louis," she said. "I'll tie them on the branches." She worked quickly. In a little while six trapezes were swinging from the largest branches of the tree.

"There," said Babe, climbing down. "That should do it. Now let's go put on our costumes."

A few minutes later Mrs. Didrikson looked out of her kitchen window. "My goodness!" she exclaimed. She hurried to the back door, wiping her hands on her apron as she went. Opening the screen door, she called, "Babe, Bubba, Louis, Lillie! Come here!" The children ran to the back steps.

"What in the world are you doing in the back yard in your long winter underwear?" asked Mrs. Didrikson.

"It's all right, Momma," said Babe. "We've got our clothes on underneath. We had to put on our union suits because we're being circus acrobats and these are our tights. We've got trapezes all over the chinaberry tree. We're learning how to swing from one to another."

Mrs. Didrikson started laughing. "All right," she said. "You circus acrobats can go on. I hadn't realized those were costumes you were wearing. I thought they were just plain underwear." She went back inside, still laughing.

Babe, Bubba, Lillie, and Louis happily went back to their tree. Babe was learning to swing from one trapeze to the next. She had already learned how to let her legs slide down along the rope until she was hanging by her feet.

"Louis, you hang by your knees from that swing," Babe said. "I'll get on this swing and jump. You try to catch my hands."

"Okay," said Louis. "I'll try, only I hope you don't pull us both down."

Babe swung back and forth. Then she jumped. She just missed Louis's outstretched hands. Ka-wham! She landed on the ground hard.

Mrs. Didrikson was watching through the kitchen window as she worked. Her heart stood still when she saw Babe hit the ground so hard. Then she breathed a sigh of relief as Babe bounced up. Her hands went back to work. "That Babe!" she said. "Nothing stops her."

A few days later the inhabitants of Doucette Street heard a loud *boom-boom-boom.* When they looked out their windows, they saw Babe. She was strutting down the street as if she were leading a parade. She carried a big washtub and was hitting it with a stick.

"Come one, come all!" she cried. She was imitating the circus barkers she had heard. "The greatest show on earth is going to be held in the Didrikson backyard right here on Doucette Street!" *Boom! Boom! Boom!* "The show will start in just a few minutes. Come one, come all!"

When the young drummer had attracted a fair number of neighborhood children, she started back toward her own house. Still banging on the washtub, she led the group into the yard.

"Now," said Babe, "you all sit right here in front of the chinaberry tree. Don't sit too close, Mike," she said to one small boy. "You have to leave room for the performers." She turned toward the house. "I'm going inside to put on my costume. I'll be right back."

In a few minutes Babe came out. She was wearing her union suit. Lillie, Louis, and Bubba followed her. They were wearing their union suits, too.

They walked in a line to the chinaberry tree. Each one took his place by a trapeze. "You will now see the One and Only Flying Didriksons!" announced Babe. Then the four of them climbed up on their swings.

They started swinging back and forth together. "Okay—*now!*" called Babe. They all slid over backwards and kept on swinging upside down. They were hanging by their knees.

After a few minutes Bubba sat up again. Then Lillie did. Babe yelled "Now!" again. This time she and Louis slipped further down until they were hanging by their feet. After that they all got off. The little crowd of children applauded.

"Wait, that's not all," said Babe. "I can do lots of other things." And she did. She threw herself from swing to swing. Once she missed and landed with a hard *smack* on the ground.

Everybody gasped, but Babe got right up and went on.

She held on to the swing with one hand and twisted around and around. She swung standing on her head. She had a wonderful time and so did her little audience.

Suddenly a voice called from the street, "Mike! Charlie! Suppertime! Come on home!" Almost at once other mothers began to call. The audience got up and hurried off to wash its hands before supper.

"Oh, here comes Poppa," cried Babe. She ran to meet him. "Poppa, Poppa," she said, taking his arm, "come see our circus! We'll put on another whole show for you."

"What's this?" said Poppa. He smiled down at his enthusiastic daughter. "Do we have a circus in our yard? Then I'll certainly have to see it. Wait a minute. I'll go get Momma to come, too."

In a few minutes Mr. and Mrs. Didrikson, Dora, Esther Nancy, and Young Ole were gathered in front of the chinaberry tree. In her best circus barker manner Babe announced "The One and Only Flying Didriksons!"

The show began again. This time there was much more applause. Poppa laughed and led the clapping at the end of each trick.

Such a good audience made Babe outdo herself. She swung higher and harder than ever. She turned longer and faster as she swung by one arm. She flung herself from swing to swing with greater recklessness.

She would have gone on and on, but finally Momma stood up. She said, "That's fine, Babe. It's been a very good show, but supper's ready and waiting on the stove."

Poppa stood up, too. He turned around and faced the rest of the audience. "Ladies and Gentlemen," he said, "you have just seen the Flying

Didriksons in another of their wonderful performances.

"Now that the show is over, I shall perform a little performance of my own. I shall do a magic trick." He waved his hands over the heads of Babe, Bubba, Lillie, and Louis.

He said, "Now you shall see, right before your very eyes the Flying Didriksons change into, first, The Walking Didriksons, and then, a few minutes later, The Eating Didriksons!"

Everybody laughed and clapped. Babe led the others running toward the house. Mr. and Mrs. Didrikson walked more slowly.

"Ole," said Mrs. Didrikson, "I worry about Babe, throwing herself around in that tree like that. I'm afraid she'll hurt herself."

Mr. Didrikson laughed. He put his arm around her shoulder. "I don't think you have to worry, Momma," he said. "Babe will be all right. It's the tree I'm not sure will survive!"

Babe Works for What She Wants

IT WAS Friday. The front door of the house on Doucette Street slammed. "Hey, Momma," said Lillie. "Have you seen Babe? The boys are playing baseball in front of Montalbano's. I thought sure she'd be there, but she's not."

"I saw her going toward the sleeping porch a little while ago, Lillie," answered her mother. "I haven't seen her since."

Lillie rushed out to the big section of the sleeping porch that was the girls' bedroom. At the doorway she stopped short. There was Babe lying on her stomach on her bed.

"What's the matter, Babe?" asked Lillie.

Babe turned over. "Nothing's the matter," she said. "I'm just listening to the radio."

"Oh," said Lillie, relieved. She sat down on the edge of the bed. "I can see the earphones now." At that time people used earphones to listen to radios, or crystal sets as they were called.

"There's a big baseball game in front of the Montalbano's," Lillie said. "I knew you'd want to know." She stood up. "Let's go."

Babe hardly heard her. She was concentrating on the radio. "You go on," she said. "I'll come out after this program."

Lillie was surprised. "What in the world are you listening to?" she asked.

"It's somebody called Castor Oil Clarence playing the harmonica. Boy, he's really something!" replied Babe.

Lillie saw Babe was completely absorbed in her program. She left and went on outside.

Babe continued to listen. When the program

was over, she sat up. A sudden look of determination lighted her face. "I'm going to learn how to play one of those things!" she said. Then she hurried out to join in the baseball game.

That night as she, Lillie, and Louis were walking back home, she said, "I'm going to get myself a harmonica."

"A harmonica?" said Louis. "What do you want one of those for? You can't play it."

"I'm going to learn how," said Babe.

"How are you going to get the money to buy one?" asked Lillie. "You know Momma and Poppa can't buy things like that."

"I know," said Babe. "I'll have to get a job and earn enough to buy it."

Lillie didn't ask her how. She knew Babe well enough to know that when Babe really wanted something, she usually found a way.

The next morning Babe set out to look for her job. She wasn't sure what she was looking for, so she just roamed the neighborhood. She was several blocks from home when she stopped.

A yard had caught her attention. The owners had just come back from a trip. The grass was very high. Maybe this could be her job!

Babe walked up to the door. The owner of the house answered her knock. "Oh—hello," he said, looking down at the small wiry figure on his doorstep.

"Mr. McClain," she said, "could I please mow your grass? I'm trying to earn some money."

"Oh?" said Mr. McClain, with a smile. "Now, let's see," he said, sitting down on the steps. "You're the littlest Didrikson girl, aren't you?"

"Yes, sir," said Babe, sitting down beside him. "Everybody calls me Babe. I want to earn enough money to buy a harmonica."

"I see," said Mr. McClain. "Do you know how to play a harmonica?"

"No, sir," answered Babe, "but I'm going to

learn. I've been listening to Castor Oil Clarence on the radio. I'm going to work real hard so I can play like he does. Would you let me mow your grass—please?"

Mr. McClain looked at his yard. "Well," he said, "we've been away quite awhile. You can see how high the grass is. I'm afraid it will be too big a job for a small girl all by herself."

"Oh, no, sir," said Babe, jumping up. "Please let me try it! I know I can do it."

Mr. McClain stood up. "You must want that harmonica pretty badly," he said smiling. "All right—go ahead and try it." He turned to go in. "By the way," he said, pausing with the screen door open. "How much does a good harmonica cost?"

"My big brother Ole told me I would have to have a quarter to get a really good one, but that I could get one for fifteen cents," she said. Twenty-five cents was a lot of money in the 1920's.

Children usually got their money only a penny at a time and then not too often.

"If you manage to cut this grass," said Mr. McClain, "you shall have enough money to buy a *good* harmonica!" He smiled and went inside.

"Oh, boy!" shouted Babe. She was so happy she turned two cartwheels just for fun. Then she went dashing down the McClain front walk.

In a little while she was back, carefully rolling her poppa's lawn mower. She turned into the McLain yard and started to work.

She pushed and shoved the mower in the tall grass. It would go only a few inches. Then the grass and the long weeds wrapping around the cutting blades would stop it. Finally Babe sat down. "It's no use," she said to herself.

Suddenly she jumped up again. "I know!" she said excitedly. "I can use that curved knife thing Ole used once on the weeds by the back fence!" She dashed home.

Soon she was back with the sickle. If Mr. McClain had looked out of his window right then he might not have let her use it. It was a very sharp, dangerous-looking instrument. One had to know just how to use it.

Babe had seen her big brother Ole use it several times and she had heard Poppa telling him how to use it. She tried to do just as she had heard Poppa say and had seen Ole do. Because she was always good at anything athletic, she got the rhythm right after only a few swings.

In a few minutes she was cutting away with enthusiasm and skill. She looked as though she had been handling a sickle for a long time. Every now and then she had to rest. It was very hard work, but she kept at it. Except for the little rests, she didn't stop a minute except to go home to eat lunch. Then she hurried right back.

It was already the middle of the afternoon when she finished cutting the high weeds and grass with the sickle. She was sitting down resting a while when a boy she knew came by.

"My goodness, Babe," he said, "what are you doing over here? We've been all up and down Doucette Street looking for you all afternoon. We wanted you to play ball with us."

"I can't go now, Johnny," she said. "I'm earning some money for a harmonica. I've got to mow this grass. I had to cut it with a sickle before I could even start using the lawn mower."

"Gosh," said Johnny in admiration. "Those things are hard to use. But it's already the middle of the afternoon. You aren't going to do nothing but work all day Saturday, are you?"

Babe nodded her head. She stood up, stretched, and picked up the lawn mower. "I'm going to finish the job today if I have to work till midnight," she said. Off she went at top speed.

Johnny watched a few minutes. Then he turned back toward Doucette Street pounding his fist into the baseball glove he was wearing. Babe saw him leave out of the corner of her eye. She *was* getting pretty tired, and a baseball game before supper would be mighty nice.

She stood still a minute, thinking. Then she turned back to mowing with a new burst of energy. "No, sir!" she told herself. "I'm not going to stop till I get through! I've just got to have that harmonica!"

The twilight of the long summer day was already beginning when Babe mowed the last little strip of tall grass. "Whew!" she said, wiping her forehead. It had been a long hard job. She surveyed the yard. "It looks pretty good," she thought. "I'm sure Mr. McClain will give me fifteen cents—and maybe even twenty-five!"

She ran toward the front porch. Just then Mr. McClain opened the screen door and came out. Evidently he had been watching her.

"Well, Babe," he said, "that surely is a good

job. I must admit I wasn't sure you would be able to do it."

Babe grinned broadly. "I guess I usually pretty well finish what I start," she said.

Mr. McClain smiled. He put his hand in his pocket. "Here," he said. He put some coins into Babe's hand. "Get yourself a first-class harmonica in return for a first-class job."

Babe looked down at the money. One, two, three, four, five, six, *seven* nickles—thirty-five cents! That was the most money of her own she had ever had in her whole life!

"Golly, Mr. McClain!" she said. She looked up at him with a radiant smile. "I ought to be able to get as good a harmonica as Castor Oil Clarence himself with all this!" she said. "Thank you—thank you very much!" In another minute she was hurrying home.

Babe could hardly eat her supper. The stores stayed open late on Saturday nights and Ole had

promised to go downtown with her to pick out her harmonica.

Babe finished her supper first. She kept coming back into the dining room to see if Ole were finished yet.

"My goodness, Ole," she said, "aren't you ever going to get through?"

Ole laughed good-naturedly. He wiped his mouth with his napkin and said, "I might just as well quit, I guess. I'm not going to have a minute's peace until I take this nuisance downtown." He pushed back his chair. "All right, Babe," he said. "Let's go."

Sometime later the Didrikson family were sitting on their front porch. They were enjoying the restful period between supper and bedtime. Suddenly Louis said, "Listen!"

Everybody on the Didrikson porch stopped rocking or swinging or talking. They listened. In the distance they could hear a harmonica.

The sounds it was making couldn't be called music, but someone was certainly playing it with enthusiasm.

"Babe!" shouted Lillie and Louis together. Off they shot down the street, followed by Bubba. A few minutes later the little group came in sight. Babe was leading the small procession. She was blowing away on her harmonica, sliding it back and forth vigorously.

Even though the noises coming out sounded very different from Castor Oil Clarence, you could tell by Babe's expression that she thought they were wonderful.

"Let me see that new harmonica, Babe," said Poppa. He turned it over in his hand and looked at it carefully. "Well," he said, "it looks as though you and Ole picked out a very nice one indeed."

Poppa blew a little on it. "Yes, indeed, very nice," he said again. "I think I'll stick to the violin, though," he added, smiling. "If you practice real hard maybe you'll be able to play with the rest of us sometime soon."

All the Didriksons were musical. Mrs. Didrikson sang. Ole played the drums. The two oldest sisters played the piano and the violin. And Poppa played the violin, too.

"I surely am going to try," said Babe. Off she went to the girls' room, blowing on her harmonica as she went.

"I don't know if any of us are going to be able to sleep tonight," said Ole, grinning. "I think Babe's going to practice right on through!"

Babe didn't practice all night, but she surely did practice a lot. Poppa had put up a hammock in the backyard now that summer had come. Babe would lie in the hammock and practice for hours at a time.

One day she came running into the kitchen. "Listen, Momma," she said excitedly. She put the harmonica to her mouth and began to play.

"Why, Babe, that's wonderful!" said Mrs. Didrikson. "That's 'Home Sweet Home'—I can recognize it."

"Yes, ma'am," said Babe, her eyes shining. "And that's not all, Momma—I can play 'Way Down Upon the Swanee River' and 'Old Black Joe', too, and parts of other things! Do you think I can play with the others now?" she asked.

"I certainly do," said Momma, patting her head. "Why don't you play with them tonight?"

Often on summer evenings the Didriksons sat on their porch after supper and played and sang. It was a kind of little family orchestra. The neighbors would hurry up and finish with the supper dishes so they could sit on their front porches and listen. The neighborhood children would sit in the Didriksons' front yard.

"All right," said Babe, "but don't tell anybody."

"I won't," said Momma.

Babe could hardly wait for everyone to finish

supper that night. She was anxious for them to start their "concert." Finally everybody was through and the dishes were washed.

"My goodness, Momma," said Esther Nancy, "what's the matter with Babe? I've never seen her so anxious to help clear the table and wash the dishes before."

Momma laughed. "I guess she's anxious for you all to start your music. By the way, Ole," she said, turning to Mr. Didrikson, "how about starting off with 'Home, Sweet Home' tonight? I always enjoy that."

"All right," said Poppa. "Let's get started then if everybody's through in the kitchen." In a few minutes everyone but Babe was on the front porch. "Where's Babe?" asked Poppa.

"Oh, I guess she'll be along in a few minutes," said Momma. "Go ahead and start. She'll come out in a minute."

"All right," said Poppa. "Here we go—'Home,

Sweet Home,' everybody." He tapped his foot and waved his bow to set the beat. The music started.

Then the screen door opened. Out came Babe. She was playing her harmonica full volume. The members of the little "orchestra" looked up in surprise. Their music stopped for a minute. Babe's melody sang out loud, clear and true in the silence.

The others took up the tune again. They all played away together. Babe was so pleased to be able to join in that she almost danced while she was playing. When the piece was over Poppa said, "Come here and let me hug you, my girl! That's mighty good playing for an eight-year-old. I'm proud of you. You're ready to play with us now—sit over there next to Lillie."

Babe just beamed. She took her place, a regular member of the family "orchestra." "Castor Oil Clarence, here I come!" she said.

Doucette Street Quarterback

"HEY, MOMMA, where's Babe?" The screen door slammed behind Louis as he ran into the house.

Mrs. Didrikson looked up from her mixing bowl. "She's doing her part of the ironing," she said. "She can't go outside until she's through, either," she called after him as he ran off.

Mrs. Didrikson put down her wooden spoon. "I'd better go and check," she said to herself. "Babe may be fourteen years old, but she still finds it hard to keep from going outside to play whether she's finished with her chores or not."

Mrs. Didrikson met Louis and Babe at the door. "I've finished, Momma," she said, as soon as she saw Momma. "Honest I have! Come and see." She led the way back to the girls' part of the sleeping porch. "There—you see!" Babe pointed to a neat pile of boys' shirts, all ironed and folded. "And the basket's empty."

Mrs. Didrikson inspected both the ironed shirts and the empty basket. Then she turned to Babe. She was smiling. "That's fine—you did a very good job. Now you may go out to play."

"Thanks, Momma." Babe gave her a quick hug. "Come on, Louis," she said.

"Now what's this you were saying about these new kids?" Babe asked.

"Well," said Louis, "they're a bunch of boys from somewhere over on the other side of town. We were waiting for you to come so we could start our game. When these guys found out that the captain of our football team was a girl—well, you should have heard them!

"They kept talking about what a sorry bunch

we must be to have a girl for a captain and all that. That's when we knew they weren't from anywhere around here or they'd have known about you. Then Jimmy whispered to me to hurry and get you. He wanted us to get started playing before somebody told them about you."

"Okay—let's hurry," said Babe. She put on a little extra burst of speed. A few minutes later they reached the vacant lot. The waiting groups of boys looked up.

"Now don't tell me that's your captain! She doesn't look like much to me," jeered one of the newcomers, a boy named Al.

It was true that Babe didn't look very impressive. She was wearing blue jeans (she loved wearing boys' clothes) and had her short, straight hair pushed behind her ears. She looked like a rather small boy.

Babe just grinned. "We'll see what you have to say about that after the game, Mister!"

The Doucette neighborhood team crowded around Babe. "What position are you going to play today, Babe?" they asked.

"Well, since Jimmy's here, he can start out as quarterback. I'll play end. Charlie, you play center. Mickey, you be right guard." Babe went on lining up her players. In a few minutes the two teams were ready to go.

The visitors, who called themselves "Al's Alligators," yelled, "Well, come on. Let's see how long that captain of yours is going to last once we get going." The Alligators didn't have to wait long to see Babe in action.

As soon as the ball was snapped, Jimmy stepped back. He waited a second until he could see Babe in the open. That didn't take long because none of the Alligators was paying much attention to her anyway.

Then Jimmy threw a long pass. Babe leaped into the air. She grabbed it! Down she came, ball in hand. Off she went. None of the Alligators was anywhere near her when she raced across the goal line for a touchdown.

"You were lucky that time!" yelled Al. Babe laughed. She was just getting into position when there was a call from the side of the field.

"Jimmy—you Jimmy!" said a voice. "Mamma says you come right home! We're supposed to leave in ten minutes."

"Oh-oh," said Jimmy. "That's my sister. Mamma's taking us downtown to meet Papa. I'd forgotten all about it. I'm sorry, Babe."

The Alligators were standing up in their positions waiting. "You all want to call it quits now?" asked Al with a smirk. "Even you guys can't do much without a quarterback, you know."

"Oh, we've got a quarterback," said Babe, smiling. She pointed to herself. "Me."

"You!" Al and the rest of the team burst into loud laughs. "Boy, is this going to be a pushover!"

It didn't take them long to find out how wrong they were. Babe carried the ball on the very first play. Even though the whole Alligator team went after her, they couldn't lay a hand on her. She outran them all. Another touchdown!

The rest of the game went the same way. Babe was everywhere. She outran, outpassed, and even outkicked all the boys on the teams.

At last the game was over. Just at that time Bubba came to call Babe and Louis home to supper. They left right away, but most of the other boys stayed around.

Al started talking to Mike, one of the boys on Babe's team. "Boy," he said, shaking his head, "I've never seen *any* kid—boy or girl—play football like that before!"

"Yeah," said Mike. "She's some athlete. She organized our football team. She plays end, fullback, and quarterback. Then we've got a baseball team she organized, too."

"What does she play on that?" asked Al.

"She plays third and shortstop sometimes, but she likes to pitch best of all."

"Is she as good in baseball as she is in football?" asked Al.

"Yes," said Mike. "She's so good they make her bat left-handed when she plays on a girls' team. She's good in everything. She can skate circles around the rest of us. She has won a couple of city swimming matches. She played tennis only three days, then entered a tournament and won it. She can run faster than anybody else. Well, you name it and she can do it."

"Does she box?" asked Al.

"She used to when she was a little kid, but she doesn't any more." Mike grinned. "I wouldn't cross her, though, even now," he said. He was quiet a moment. "She says she's going to be the world's greatest athlete," he added.

"Well, I'll tell you," said Al, "if anybody had

told me yesterday that a girl had said that, I'd have just about killed myself laughing. Today I'm not even smiling."

By this time Babe was at home. She was lying on her stomach on the living room floor. She was looking at the newspaper.

Lillie came in from the kitchen. "What are you doing?" she asked.

"I'm reading about the Olympics," said Babe. "Poppa was telling me about them last night. The United States sends a team, Norway sends a team, every country sends a team. All the best athletes from all over the world come together and compete.

"It sounds like just about the most wonderful thing that ever happened. I've decided I'm going to be in the Olympics myself."

Hurdling the Hedges

"POPPA!" BABE ran down the front steps to meet her father. She had been waiting for him to come home from work.

"Hello, Babe," he said. He gave her a kiss. He could tell by the way her eyes were shining that she was excited about something. "What is it?" he asked.

"I've been reading all about the Olympics in the paper," she said. "I've decided I'm going to be in them next year!"

Poppa smiled. "I'm afraid not, Babe," he said.

Babe stopped short. "Why?" she asked. "There isn't any age limit or anything, is there?

Anyway I'll be sixteen by this time next year. That surely ought to be old enough."

Poppa smiled again. "There's no age limit that I know of," he said. "But the reason you can't be in the Olympics next year is that there won't be any Olympics next year. They are held only once every four years."

"Oh," said Babe, her face falling. Then she brightened. "Well, I guess that will just give me that much more time to get ready," she said in a determined voice.

"That's the spirit," said Poppa approvingly. He and Babe went into the house.

"Hey, Lillie," said Babe. "Poppa says there won't be any Olympics next year. We'll have to wait four years for the next one. There won't be another one till 1932."

"Oh," said Lillie, "that's too bad."

"It'll be all right," said Babe. "There'll just be more time to get ready." She turned to her father. "Lillie thinks she might be in the Olympics, too," she said. "She can run faster than anybody else in our neighborhood, Poppa." She looked at her sister. "I'll tell you what, Lillie—you run and I'll jump!"

"All right!" said Lillie.

"We'll have to start working out right away," said Babe. At that moment Mrs. Didrickson came into the room.

"Babe," she said, "I want you and Lillie to run down to the store for me. Here's a list of things we need."

"All right, Momma," said Babe. She had an idea. "Say, we can start our practicing right now, Lillie. I'll jump the hedges between the yards from here to the store. You can run on the sidewalk. We can have a race."

"Perhaps you can do that on your way back from the store," said Poppa. "On your way to the store I want you to stop and ask each person's permission to run through his yard and jump over his hedge."

"Yes, sir," said Babe. A few minutes later she was knocking at the door of one of the neighbors.

"Hello, Mrs. Goodman," she said when the door was opened. "Lillie and I are training for the Olympics. We'd like to be able to run through your yard and practice, please ma'am."

"The Olympics?" Mrs. Goodman looked interested.

"Not the ones right now," said Babe quickly, "the next ones."

"Oh," said Mrs. Goodman, "the 1932 Olympics. I see. Are you and Lillie going to be runners?" she asked.

"Lillie is," said Babe, "but I'm going to be a jumper. That's why I have to run through your yard—if it's all right, that is, Mrs. Goodman. I want to use the hedges as hurdles."

Mrs. Goodman looked at her hedge. "Well, if

you can jump over the hedges along this block you certainly shouldn't have any trouble with hurdles. A hurdle is only about a half-inch thick, but these hedges are a good two feet across!"

"Oh, that's all right," said Babe. "I'm sure I won't have any trouble with them."

"Babe never opens a gate if she can jump over it instead," put in Lillie.

"Is it all right if we use your yard, Mrs. Goodman?" asked Babe.

"Certainly it's all right, Babe," replied Mrs. Goodman. "And I'll be waiting to hear how you come out in the 1932 Olympics." She smiled and went back inside her house.

Babe and Lillie went on down the block. Babe asked each neighbor if she could run through his yard. Finally they had everybody's permission. By this time they were almost to the store. They hurried to get the things on Mrs. Didrikson's list.

"Now!" said Babe. "We're ready. Lillie, you run on the pavement. I'll run through the yards and hurdle the hedges. We'll see who gets home first."

Lillie grinned. "You're good, Babe," she said, "but you're not that good. I'm bound to get there first with you having to jump over the hedges."

Babe grinned back. "Maybe now," she said, "but you better watch out later on! Okay—get on your mark—get set—go!"

Off they raced! Babe went hurdling over those hedges. She had to hold her front knee up extra high, she discovered. Otherwise she would get scraped.

Lillie raced along the pavement. She got home first, dashed across the yard, and sat down on the steps. In a few minutes Babe came sailing over the last hedge.

"What happened to you?" asked Lillie, grinning. "It surely did take you a long time."

Babe threw herself down on the steps next to Lillie. "Yeah," she said, "you've been here for hours, haven't you?" They both laughed.

"I really was slowed up, though," said Babe. "One of the hedges is higher than the others. I guess I'll get used to it, though."

After that hardly a day passed without several races between Babe and Lillie. One night after supper Poppa asked, "How's the Olympic training coming?"

"We're working on it," said Babe. "Lillie still wins, but I'm gaining on her." Lillie smiled.

Babe went on. "I could do lots better, Poppa, if all the hedges were the same height. The Kings' hedge is higher than the rest. I have an awful time getting over it. I'm always landing on it or getting caught on it or something. I've been thinking I might go ask Mr. King to cut it down even with the rest."

Mr. Didrikson thought a minute. "I think it

would be all right to ask him. If you explain why you want him to, he probably wouldn't mind."

"I think I'll go right now," said Babe. She jumped up. In a few seconds she was knocking at Mr. King's front door.

"Yes?" said Mr. King, opening the door. "Oh, hello, Babe," he added as he recognized her.

"Mr. King," said Babe, "you remember when I came over to ask if I could run across your yard and jump over your hedge? I told you I was training for the Olympics."

"I remember," said Mr. King, smiling. "I've seen you practicing, too. But I notice you seem to be having a little trouble getting over."

"Well, that's what I came to talk to you about," said Babe. "Your hedge is a good bit higher than the others. The rest are all pretty much alike.

"I just can't seem to get over yours as well as I do the others. I was wondering if you'd mind very much cutting it down even with the rest."

Babe stopped. She wasn't sure how Mr. King would feel about her request.

He thought a minute. He looked at his hedge. He looked at the other hedges he could see.

"Why, yes, Babe," he said. "I wouldn't mind doing that."

Babe breathed a sigh of relief. "I surely do thank you, Mr. King," she said.

The next day Babe and Lillie had to go to the store. Babe raced along, running and hurdling.

She was almost at the store before she realized Mr. King had already cut his hedge!

"Okay, Lillie," she said, when they got to the store. "You'd better watch out from now on!"

They raced along Doucette Street. Lillie raced along the sidewalk. Babe raced through the yards and soared over the hedges. "Boy, it's really fun now!" she thought as she sailed over the Kings' hedge.

"Almost caught up with you that time!" she shouted to Lillie. Lillie had reached the Didrikson yard just seconds before Babe. As the months went on Babe got better and better. Then one day she actually won!

After that their races were neck and neck. Lillie won most of the time, but Babe managed to get there just inches behind her. Occasionally Babe even got there first.

"Olympics, here I come!" said Babe. "I only hope the time till 1932 will hurry up and go by!"

Coach Dimmitt Lends a Hand

BABE FOUND that time did hurry by. For one thing she was in high school now. Right away the athletes in Beaumont High School noticed her presence. And it wasn't only the girl athletes!

Babe was one of only two girls ever to make the girls' basketball team in her freshman year. Everybody thought she was very good. Babe wasn't satisfied, though. From the beginning of the school year she felt she should be learning more about the sport.

Then she had an idea. "I know what I'll do," she said to herself. "I'll go see Coach Dimitt. He knows more about basketball and everything else than any of these others know. Boys always know more about basketball than girls do, anyhow." At that time the girls played basketball by the same rules as the boys.

Babe ran off to find Coach Lilburn Dimmitt. He was the head coach and athletic director of Beaumont High School. When she found him he was busy working with the boys' basketball team. She sat down on a bench and watched. Babe wasn't much interested in boys as dates or boy friends, but she was very much interested in them as athletes.

After a little while Coach Dimmitt saw her. "Hello," he said. "What can I do for you?"

"Coach," said Babe, "I want to learn all I can about sports. How about letting me work out with your boys' teams?"

Coach Dimmitt had heard something of Babe's athletic abilities. He had seen her practicing with the girls' basketball team. He was interested. "All right, Babe," he said. "We're just finishing up for today. Suppose you come by when you have some free time tomorrow."

"Thanks, Coach," said Babe, grinning happily. "Thanks a lot."

The next day during study hall Babe worked very hard. She rushed through her homework. Then she went up to the study hall teacher. "Miss Winters," she said, "may I go down to the gym and practice basketball now? I've finished all my homework." Babe held out her notebook.

Miss Winters looked carefully at the different pages Babe showed her. "All right, Babe," she said. "You may go since you have completed all your work."

"Thank you, ma'am," said Babe. Minutes later she was running down to the gym. She fairly jumped into her gym suit.

"Here I am, Coacher," she said to Mr. Dimmitt.

"Oh—Babe," he said. "I didn't expect to see you now. Don't you have class?"

"No, sir," she answered. "I have study hall now. Miss Winters said I could come and practice because I had all my homework done."

"That's all right, then," he said.

"Could you show me how to pivot, Coacher?" asked Babe. "I've been practicing, but I don't know whether I'm doing it right. Is this the way?" Then Babe ran out and began to practice.

That was the first of many, many sessions. Every spare minute she had Babe spent with Coach Dimmitt—"Coacher," she called him. She was always saying, "Watch me, Coacher!" or "Did I do that right?" Coach Dimmitt was always ready to help her.

One day several of the boys from the basketball team were standing with Coach Dimmitt. They were all watching Babe and some of the boy basketball players practicing. One of the boys said, "Boy, that Babe just doesn't stop, does she? I never saw anybody stick to something the way she does."

"Yes," said Coach Dimmitt. "That's one thing about her that impresses me. She has great natural ability, but what really sets her apart is the way she's willing to work. She'll practice for hours on anything you suggest. She'll work until she has even the smallest detail just right."

Johnny Radford was the captain of the boys' basketball team. "One thing I like is the way she doesn't ask any favors," he said. "She takes the bumps with the rest of us. And gives them, too!" he added with a grin. He and the others watched a few minutes more. Then he said, "We sure could use her on our team."

Babe not only learned a lot about basketball from Coach Dimmitt. He let her work out with his boys in almost all their sports. She could even outkick their best extra-point kicker on the football team. It was Coach Dimmitt who gave Babe her first real groundwork in all the sports.

One day Babe was walking home. She heard someone call her. "Hey, Babe, wait a minute! I've got your *Pine Burr* for you."

Babe turned around. "Hi, Roady," she said. "Thanks for bringing my *Pine Burr*. I hadn't known it was ready." The *Pine Burr* was the Beaumont High School annual.

"Why don't we go down to Doc Pierce's and have a malt while we look?" said Roady.

"Okay," said Babe.

A few minutes later the two girls were seated in a booth in "Doc" Pierce's drugstore. "Hello, ladies," said Mr. Pierce. "What'll it be?"

"The usual thing for me, Doc," said Babe. "How about you, Roady?"

"Me, too," said Roady.

"Two chicken salad sandwiches and two malted milks coming up," said Doc.

Babe was already leafing through her *Pine Burr*. "Hey, Roady," she said. "Here you are. I'll read it:

"PEARL ANDRUS, center, forward.

> " 'Roady' is small, but she is an excellent basketball player, a girl who can pass, catch, and pivot with rare skill. Her ability on the court, combined with a likeable manner and a ready supply of wit, has made her a pal of all.

"That's very nice, Roady," said Babe.

Roady grinned. "Thanks, Babe," she said. "I've found yours. First it lists the five varsity sports you lettered in: girls' basketball, girls' baseball, girls' volleyball, girls' golf team, and girls' tennis team." Roady looked up at Babe and grinned. "It's too bad they didn't let you try out for the boys' teams, too—you'd have had *ten* varsity letters!"

Babe laughed.

"Here's what it says under your picture," said Roady. She read:

> " 'Babe' has been a very necessary player on the Miss Royal Purple squad this year. She never failed to star in any game, at home or abroad. She is a very capable forward who very seldom misses a basket. When Babe gets the ball, the scorekeeper gets his adding machine, and then he loses count."

"Oh, here come our sandwiches," said Babe.

It was just about true that the scorekeepers needed adding machines when Babe played. She was scoring twenty-five, thirty, and even forty points in a game. After almost every game there were writeups in the Beaumont paper. Mrs. Didrikson started keeping a scrapbook of Babe's clippings.

One night Poppa came in all excited. "Where's Babe, Momma?" he asked. Mrs. Didrikson looked up from the meatballs she was making.

"I don't know, Ole," she said. "I guess she's still practicing basketball at school. Why? Has anything happened?"

Poppa smiled. "It surely has," he said. "I've really got an item for that scrapbook you're making." Just then the front screen door slammed.

"Hey, I'm home," Babe said. She walked into the kitchen. "Hello, Momma. Hello, Poppa," she said, kissing each of them. "Is it almost suppertime? I'm starved. I've been thinking about eating all the way home."

Poppa smiled. "I'll bet I have something that will make you stop thinking of eating for awhile," he said. He reminded Babe of the cat that swallowed the canary. "Here, look at this." With a grand gesture he opened the paper to the sports page and held it before Babe.

Babe read:

"DIDRIKSON NAMED ALL-CITY, ALL-STATE IN BASKETBALL!"

Enter Colonel McCombs

Meanwhile in Dallas someone else was reading those very same headlines. That someone was a Colonel M. J. McCombs. Just then he was saying, "John, I think I'll have to take a trip over to Houston next week. I see the Beaumont High girls' team is playing Houston Heights High School. I want to see this Babe Didrikson."

"If she's as good as the papers say she is," said John, "she'd really be quite an addition to our company basketball team."

Colonel McCombs was the head of a department of the Employers Casualty Company, an insurance firm. He was also in charge of the women's athletic program for the company, and that was why he was interested in Babe.

"Yes, indeed," he said. "Any girl who can score thirty and forty points in one game is well worth taking a look at. I think I'll definitely go over to Houston next week."

Babe was already thinking about the game against Houston Heights, too. "Everybody says they're supposed to be pretty tough," she told her father.

"It ought to be a good game then," said Mr. Didrikson. "I think I'll try to go over with you to see it."

"Oh, Poppa, would you?" cried Babe. "That would be just wonderful!"

So the following week both Mr. Didrikson and Colonel McCombs were in Houston watching Babe play basketball.

"My goodness!" said Poppa to himself when the Houston Heights girls came out onto the court. "Those are really big, tall girls." He shook his head. "I'm afraid Beaumont's going to have a hard time."

As soon as the game started, though, he saw things weren't going to be so bad as he had been afraid they might. Babe wasn't as tall as some of the Houston Heights girls, but she was fast as greased lightning. She just sailed around her opponents. Before the game was over, she had scored twenty-six points.

Babe was standing by the bench wiping her face with a towel when a man came up.

"Miss Didrikson?" he said. "I am Colonel M. J. McCombs. I just wondered if you would be interested in playing on a big city team."

"Boy, I'll say I would!" exclaimed Babe. "Where?"

"In Dallas. I work for the Employers Casualty Company there and I'm in charge of women's athletics for the firm."

"Golly," said Babe, "what would I have to do? School won't be out for some time yet."

"Well," said Colonel McCombs, "first we'll have to ask your parents' permission. If it's all right with them, we'll arrange for you to get out of school for awhile."

"Poppa's here today," said Babe. "In fact, here he comes right now." She pointed to the stands. Mr. Didrikson was just making his way down from his seat to the court. Babe ran over to meet him. "Poppa," she said excitedly, "this is Colonel McCombs from Dallas and he wants to know if I can go over there and play basketball for his team!"

The two men shook hands. Poppa looked questioningly at Colonel McCombs.

Colonel McCombs said, "Our women's basketball team from the Employers Casualty Company finished second last year in the Women's National A.A.U. Tournament. We're going to the nationals again this year—in March in fact. I think Babe could help us come in first. We'd like for her to come to Dallas, join the company, and play basketball for us. How about it?"

"Well," said Mr. Didrikson, "Dallas is quite a distance from Beaumont. I'm not sure Babe's momma would be willing to let her go."

"Oh, Poppa, please!" said Babe. "Please say I can go."

Her father put his arm around her shoulders. "We'll have to ask Momma, Babe," he said.

"I know what," said Colonel McCombs. "Let me drive you down to Beaumont and we can talk to your mother right away. Time is pretty important to us. It's already February and the national tournament is next month. I'd like to get Babe on the team as soon as possible."

Mr. Didrikson agreed. In a few minutes he and Babe were riding in Colonel McComb's car.

"Golly," said Babe, "this is just about the

swankiest car I've ever ridden in or even seen. Won't Momma and Lillie be surprised when they see us come riding up to the house in it, Poppa?" she asked.

"They probably will," Poppa said with a smile. He settled himself comfortably in his seat and looked out the window. "It's some distance from Houston to Beaumont," he went on. "We might as well enjoy riding in such a fancy car."

Before long Colonel McCombs had left Houston and was out on the highway speeding eastward toward Beaumont.

"Babe, do you play anything besides basketball?" he asked presently.

Babe grinned. "I play them all," she said. "You name it and I'll play it. I wouldn't say that I'm good at everything, but there isn't any sport that I don't enjoy."

The Colonel laughed, and Babe settled back to enjoy the ride with Poppa.

Finally they reached Beaumont and the car rolled up in front of the Didriksons' house. Momma and Lillie *were* surprised to see Poppa and Babe step out. Poppa and Babe both started explaining at once.

"Wait, wait," said Momma. "I can't understand a thing with both of you talking at the same time. Now, Babe, you just be quiet and let Poppa talk."

"Yes, ma'am," said Babe. She didn't say anything else, but was so excited she couldn't stand still. She shifted from one foot to the other while Mr. Didrikson introduced Colonel McCombs and explained why he was there.

Momma listened quietly. Then she said, "Won't you stay for supper, Colonel McCombs? This is a very big decision. I would like to hear everything about it before we decide."

"Thank you, Mrs. Didrikson," he said. "I'd enjoy that if you're sure I wouldn't be putting you to too much trouble. I think your daughter has the makings of a really great basketball player. I'm very anxious to have her on our team. I'll be glad to give you all the information I can."

After supper when Colonel McCombs was getting ready to leave, Mr. Didrikson said, "We'll think it over, Colonel, and let you know."

"All right," said Colonel McCombs, "and I surely did enjoy those Norwegian meatballs. They were delicious."

Everybody stood on the front porch to wave good-by as the long shiny car drove away. Then Momma turned to Babe. "My Babe," she said, "do you really want to go all the way to Dallas?"

"Yes, Momma," said Babe.

Mrs. Didrikson turned to her husband. She put her hand on his shoulder. "Ole," she said, "what do you think we should do about it?"

"I think we need the advice of someone more used to this than we are," said Poppa. "I think

I'll go talk to Mr. Scurlock. He's the sports editor for the Beaumont *Journal* who's always taken such an interest in Babe. I'll see what he thinks."

Poppa came back several hours later. "Now, Babe, you be quiet," said Mrs. Didrikson. "Let Poppa and me talk a little while. What did Mr. Scurlock say, Poppa?" she asked.

"He said he thinks it would be a fine opportunity for Babe," said Mr. Didrikson. "He thinks this might be the beginning of a real career in sports for her."

Momma sat down. She was quiet for a moment. Then she asked, "And what do you think?"

"I think we ought to let her go," said Poppa.

Momma looked at Babe. "She's so young," she said. "Why, she's just sixteen years old! And Dallas is so far away. I just think she's too young to be making a trip like that all by herself."

"If it would make you feel better," said Mr. Didrikson, "I'll go with her."

"Oh, Momma, *please!*" said Babe. She had stayed quiet as long as she could.

"We-l-l—" said Mrs. Didrikson slowly. "Maybe it would be all right if your Poppa made the trip with you."

"Hurrah!" shouted Babe, leaping into the air.

"What are you going to do about school?" asked Lillie.

"Colonel McCombs told Poppa he thought I could get excused from school till after the basketball season is over," said Babe. "It's just about three more weeks. When I told him I had a pretty good average he said he was sure it could be arranged."

She turned to her father, "Can we leave tomorrow morning?" she asked eagerly. "You know Colonel McCombs said I should get there as soon as possible."

"Yes, yes," said Poppa smiling, "but we don't have to be in that much of a hurry. We have to

see the people at school. You and Momma will want to get your clothes ready. We have to let Colonel McCombs know what we decided. There's a lot of things we'll have to do."

Two days later Babe and her father went down to catch the overnight train that was to take them to Dallas.

"Golly, Babe," said Lillie, as her sister was getting ready to leave, "I don't think I've ever seen you so dressed up before." She walked around Babe. "Your State Fair dress looks mighty nice." Babe had on a blue silk dress she had made at school. It had won a prize at the Texas State Fair. She was even wearing a hat!

"Do you have your money, Babe?" asked Momma. If anyone looked closely, they could see a few tears in her eyes.

"Yes, ma'am," said Babe. "I have it in here." She patted her black patent leather purse. There was $3.49 in it. That was the change from the money for the railroad tickets. It was all the money Babe had.

At last they were off. It was the first time Babe had ever been more than a few miles from Beaumont. It was the first time she had had a real train trip. It was the first time she had seen a berth on the train. "I'm so excited I don't know whether I'll be able to sleep!" she told Poppa.

Mr. Didrikson smiled. "Don't waste these good berths," he said. He lighted his big black pipe and settled back in his lower berth. Babe had the berth just above his.

"I feel like I'm going off to Europe or something," she said leaning back. "Just think—I'll be playing on a *real* basketball team! It sounds like the beginning of everything I've always wanted to do!"

A Big Step up the Ladder

Babe was looking out of the window when the train pulled into the Dallas station the next morning. "Look, Poppa," she cried excitedly, "there's Colonel McCombs!" Poppa looked. He felt excited, too, but he tried not to show it too much.

Babe was the first person down the train steps. "Hi, Colonel McCombs!" she called. She rushed up to him.

"Hello, Babe," he replied. He turned to Poppa. "Hello, Mr. Didrikson," he said. They shook hands. "I've brought one member of the team along to meet you, Babe," he added. "This is Leona Thaxton. Leona, this is Babe Didrikson, and this is her father, Mr. Ole Didrikson. Leona plays guard on our team."

"I'm glad to meet you, Leona," said Babe.

"Now we'll go down to the company," said Colonel McCombs. "We have our offices in the Interurban Building," he told Mr. Didrikson. "Most of the girls on the team work in my department."

They got into the big yellow Cadillac. "This is the car the Colonel uses for driving the basketball team to its games," Leona told Babe.

"By the way, Babe," said Colonel McCombs, "what sort of office work can you do?"

"I've had typing and shorthand in school," said Babe. "I even got a gold medal for typing faster than anybody else. I did eighty-six words a minute," she said proudly. "I can learn to do most any kind of math, too, I think."

"Do you know how to use a slide rule?" asked Colonel McCombs.

"No, sir," said Babe, "but I'm pretty good with numbers. I'm sure I could learn real fast."

Colonel McCombs smiled. "Well, I think we'll try you out on a slide rule then," he said.

A few minutes later they drew up at the Interurban Building and went inside. "My office is in Room 327," said Colonel McCombs. He ushered them out of the elevator. "Here we are," he said, opening the door, "and here's our team, the Golden Cyclones."

Babe looked at the girls who came up to greet them. "I never saw so many big, husky girls in my life!" she told Poppa later.

Colonel McCombs introduced Babe around the room. After that he took her to the athletic supply room. "Here, Babe," he said. "The extra basketball uniforms are in here. Pick out the one you want."

"I always wore Number Seven at Beaumont High," said Babe. She was going through the things hanging on the rack. "And here's Number Seven right here!" she exclaimed.

"It's pretty big," said Colonel McCombs.

"Oh, that's all right," said Babe. "I can sew real well. I'll take it up and it will fit fine."

"Can you do it in a hurry?" the Colonel asked. "We play the Sun Oil Company team tonight. They're the national champions this year. I'd like for you to be ready to go into that game this evening. Do you think you could?"

"Sure," said Babe. "The sooner the better."

That night Babe had to go past the Sun Oilers' bench on the way to her own. She trotted along the edge of the court. One of the Sun Oil girls said, "There goes that kid from Beaumont."

"Yeah," said another teammate. "What do you say we don't let her score any points tonight?"

"Okay," agreed the first. "That shouldn't be too hard."

Babe grinned to herself. "I'll make them

change their tune!" she thought. And sure enough she did. The Sun Oilers played rough and they guarded her as closely as they could. Nevertheless, they couldn't keep Babe from scoring. In fact, she made more points by herself than the whole Sun Oil team put together!

Only a few weeks later Babe and the rest of the Employers Casualty Company were on their way to the National Tournament. "Golly," said Babe, "I sure hope we win the championship!" They didn't win, but Babe was so outstanding she was chosen for the 1930 All-American Basketball Team. That was a wonderful honor. Babe was to win it three years straight.

After that first tournament in 1930, Babe went back to Beaumont High School to finish out the year. Then it was time for her to go back to work in Dallas.

"Oh, Momma," she said, giving her mother a hug, "I'll miss all of you so much." She took a step back and looked at her mother. "But I'm so glad to be able to help out. I'll send money home every single payday." She gave each member of the family a quick strong bear-hug. Then she jumped aboard the train. The Didriksons could see her leaning out of the window waving almost as long as they could see the train.

Then Babe was back at the Employers Casualty Company once more. She made seventy-five dollars a month and sent home forty-five.

One Saturday morning Babe was working at her desk. "Things are pretty slow nowadays," she thought. "Nothing much exciting has happened since the basketball season ended."

Just then Colonel McCombs walked in. He had evidently been thinking about the same thing. "Babe," he said, "I was just wondering what you've been doing with yourself since the end of the basketball season."

"Not very much, Colonel," Babe answered.

"Well," he said, "I'm going to Lakeside Park this afternoon. There's a track meet out there. How would you like to go?"

"I'd like to," said Babe.

A little later they were at the park. They got out of the car and walked around. "Look," said Colonel McCombs, "they are getting ready for the hurdles."

Babe watched. The field attendants brought out the fence-like hurdles and set them up across the track. A few minutes later the racers started down the course.

"Boy, look at them jumping over those hurdles!" cried Babe excitedly. "That reminds me of the hedge-hopping races Lillie and I used to have."

She turned to Colonel McCombs. "Colonel," she said, "why couldn't we organize a track and field team for the girls at Employers Casualty? All of us need something to keep us busy now that basketball season is over. This would be just the thing for the summer. How about it?"

"Why, yes," said Colonel McCombs, "I think you've got a good idea there, Babe. I'll take it up with the president of the company the first thing Monday morning."

Monday afternoon Colonel McCombs called in all the girls who played on the company basketball team. Babe and the others filed into his office. Colonel McCombs told them about the plan to organize a track team.

Everybody started talking at once. "I think I'll try the high jump," said one.

"I'm going to run," said another.

"How about the javelin?" said a third. "I think I'd like to learn to throw that."

"What are you going to do, Babe?" someone asked.

Babe turned to Colonel McCombs. "How many different events are there?" she asked.

"Well, let's see," he said. "I think there are about ten or so. Why?"

"Because I'm going to try all of them," said Babe. Everybody laughed and laughed.

"That's a real good joke, Babe," said one girl.

Babe looked very serious. "I'm not joking at all," she explained. "I really mean it."

"Well," said Colonel McCombs, "everybody will have to get busy right away. We'll have our first meet week after next. You girls will be able to practice two hours every afternoon. I'll be out there to coach."

"Gee," said Babe to herself. "Two hours a day isn't very much. If I'm going to take this stuff up, I'm going to really get to work."

And she did. Every evening she changed into her exercise clothes the minute she finished dinner. She ran down a long hill near the house she lived in. Then she ran all the way back up.

Every night she went out to Lakeside Park.

All by herself she practiced and practiced. She worked until it got too dark to see. The summer days were long. Sometimes it was after nine o'clock at night before she stopped.

"Well, tomorrow's the meet," said Babe at dinner one night. All the basketball girls from

Employers Casualty ate together at a boarding-house. "I'm going out for one last practice."

"My goodness, Babe," said one of the other girls on the team, "don't tell me you're working out again tonight. I think you ought to relax."

"I've got to practice," said Babe. She got up from the table. "I have to work on my steps for the broad jump and the high jump."

The other girl shook her head. "I never saw anybody work so hard at *everything!*" she said. "Why do you do it?"

Babe grinned. "I guess that's just the way I am," she said. "When I do something, I believe in giving it everything I've got." And out she went to practice. It was three hours later before she was satisfied that she had practiced enough.

And evidently she had. The next day she entered her first track meet. She competed in four events—and she won all four! It was a dazzling beginning to a dazzling career.

The Record-Breaker

ONE DAY Babe was writing a letter. She wrote:

Dear Momma and Poppa

I've been keeping pretty busy. Besides working out for track, we have a team in the Dallas Girls' Softball League. Of course I'm on it.

I had a pretty good night Monday. We played a double-header and I hit thirteen home runs.

We're getting ready for the 1930 Track and Field A.A.U. Championships. They're going to be held right here in Dallas on the Fourth of July. I sure wish you all could come up for them.

I have to stop now. It's almost time for us to practice.

I love you all.

Babe

P.S. Here's a clipping for Momma's scrapbook.

The clipping said:

An exhibition of fancy diving and swimming stunts will be given at White Rock municipal pool Sunday afternoon from 3 until 5 o'clock by Mildred Didrikson and her Employers Casualty girls. In addition the Babe will drive a motor speed boat in some fancy arcs and later will show the populace how to handle the bounding and treacherous aquaplane.

Hurriedly Babe sealed the letter and addressed it. On her way to the practice field she dropped it into a mailbox.

It was fun being in Dallas. She was making a name for herself in all the sports she took part in. Still, there were times when she missed Beaumont and Momma, Poppa, Lillie, and all the rest very much.

She trotted onto the practice field. Her thoughts turned to track. In a few minutes she started practicing her high jump. Colonel McCombs came over to watch. He kept moving the cross bar up higher and higher. Babe kept jumping higher and higher.

"Okay, Babe," he said, moving it up again. "I've got it at five feet, three inches. That's the women's world record." He looked at Babe and grinned. "You make this one and I'll treat you to an ice cream soda. How about it?"

"Move back, everybody, here I come!" cried Babe. And over she went! "How about making that a banana split if I go higher?" she said with a grin. Then she was serious. "I think maybe I can," she added.

"All right," said Colonel McCombs. "Try it." He moved the cross bar up. Babe tried. Down went the bar. She tried several times, but she couldn't make it.

"I think," said Colonel McCombs, "that we'll have to try this new style of jumping called the Western Roll. I don't believe you'll be able to get above the record with the scissors kick you've been using."

"What's the Western Roll?" asked Babe. "I've never seen anybody use anything but the scissors kick."

"Several of the men high jumpers are beginning to use the Western Roll. You have to slide your whole body across the bar sideways," said the Colonel. "The main thing is to have your feet go over the bar first. If they don't, the jump is disqualified."

"All right," said Babe. "When do we start?" Colonel McCombs began explaining it to her. Babe set right to work. Down went the bar time after time. "I guess I'm just diving over head first," she said. She was resting a minute.

"It's going to take a lot of work," said the

Colonel. "But I think the change will be worth it in the end."

"Well, I'll get it then," said Babe firmly, "even if I have to work on it all day and all night for the next month!"

And Babe did work on it. She didn't work all day and all night, of course. But, she did practice many hours every day.

Colonel McCombs kept watching and helping. Finally the day came when he said, "Babe, that was it! Try it again just that way."

Babe tried it. "You got your feet over first again!" he cried. "Maybe we've got it at last!" And sure enough, Babe did have it. Time after time she slid across the bar easily and smoothly.

All their hours and hours of hard work had finally had results. "Hooray!" shouted Babe. And she ran and jumped over the cross bar once more, just for fun.

Even though she was working so much on the

high jump, Babe didn't forget the other events. She worked on them all. When the Fourth of July came, she was ready.

"Today's the day," she said to herself as she jumped out of bed. She was all excited. It wasn't everyday somebody got to be in the Women's National A.A.U. Championships!

It turned out to be a good day for Babe, too. She won the javelin throw. She threw the baseball farthest. That gave her two first places.

Then it was time for the broad jump. Babe took a running start and jumped.

A huge roar went up from the crowd. They could tell at once that she had jumped very far. The judges measured.

Then there was an announcement. "Miss Mildred Didrikson has just broken the women's world record in the broad jump. Her jump measured eighteen feet, eight and one-half inches." The crowd cheered again.

All the girls crowded around Babe. "Congratulations!" they cried. "Not bad for a kid who just had her seventeenth birthday last week." They patted Babe on the back. They shook her hand. Babe grinned from ear to ear.

"Here comes Stella Walsh," said one of the group. All the girls turned around to look at the world-famous athlete.

"She's going to do her jump now," said a girl.

"She's one of the best," said another, "but I guess she'll have to be satisfied with a second place this time."

Babe watched very carefully. Miss Walsh ran. She jumped. Once again there was a roar from the crowd. This was another long, long jump.

"It looks like she landed just where I did," thought Babe. She crossed her fingers.

Then came the announcement over the loud speaker. "A new world's record has just been set. Miss Stella Walsh has jumped eighteen feet, eight and three-fourths inches. Her jump is one-fourth inch longer than Miss Didrikson's record."

Babe joined in the applause. The girls standing near her said, "Golly, Babe, that's too bad," and "Tough luck." Babe managed to smile.

"Oh, well, there's always next year," she said. And when next year came around, Babe was ready. In 1931 she won three first places, and one was in the broad jump!

"I'm sorry I didn't break the record, though," said Babe, shaking her head.

Colonel McCombs smiled. "Well," he said, "I wouldn't worry about that. I think breaking two world's records is enough for one year!"

And it was true. Babe had set new records in the baseball throw and in the hurdles. She had thrown the baseball 296 feet. She had run the eighty-meter hurdles in twelve seconds flat.

"Well, Babe," said one of the girls who came up to congratulate her, "I guess you've reached the top now. You entered three events. You won first place in three events, not to mention breaking two world's records. You won't even need to come back next year!"

Babe smiled. "They'll be holding the Olympic tryouts then. I'll have to do better next year!"

"Honestly, Babe!" the girl laughed. Then she added, "I don't see how you *can* do better."

But there was someone besides Babe who was sure she could. One day Colonel McCombs called Babe into his office. "Babe," he said, "How would you like to go to the National all by yourself next summer?"

"By myself?" asked Babe.

"Yes," said the Colonel. "I've been checking all the records of the other teams that will be there. Last year one person could enter only three events. This year a person can enter as many as she wants to. I believe you can win the national championship all by yourself!"

The One-Girl Team

"MOMMA! MOMMA!" called Babe. "The car's here." She turned away from the window.

"All right, Babe," said Mrs. Didrikson. She gave the things in the suitcase a final pat. She closed the top. "Here, Bubba," she said to her youngest son, "take this out to the car."

"Yes, ma'am," said Bubba.

"It sure has been wonderful having you and Bubba up here these two weeks, Momma," said Babe. "I don't believe I could ever have got ready without you." She gave Mrs. Didrikson a big hug.

Her mother smiled. "I don't believe you could

have either. Now you do real well up there in Chicago, Babe," she added.

"I will, Momma," Babe said. She grinned. "I'll mow 'em down!"

"Everybody in Beaumont sure will be keeping up with you, Babe," said Bubba. He had just come back into the room. "Tiny Scurlock devoted his whole sports column in the Beaumont *Journal* to you last week. He even told about me and Momma coming over to Dallas."

A horn sounded. "Oh-oh," said Babe. "We'd better hurry. We don't want to miss that train. Let's go." She held the door open for her mother.

Colonel McCombs and Mrs. Wood were waiting in the car. Mrs. Wood was the Employers Casualty girls' "Team Mother." She was going with Babe to Chicago.

A few minutes later they were at the depot. "Do be careful, my girl," said Mrs. Didrikson as they walked to Babe's train.

"Don't worry, Momma," said Babe. "I can take care of myself anywhere!"

"I really think she can, Mrs. Didrikson," said Mrs. Wood, smiling. "But don't forget I'll be there, too. You mustn't worry."

"Here's where we get on," said Babe. She gave her mother and brother a last hug. " 'Bye, Momma. 'Bye, Bubba." She hopped up on the step.

"Good luck, Babe!" called Bubba, waving. "Win 'em all!"

Babe grinned. "I'll sure try, Bubba," she said. The train began to move. "Chicago, here I come!" she cried. And it wasn't long before Chicago knew Babe *had* come!

The night before the meet was to start Babe was so excited she couldn't sleep. It was very late before she finally did get to sleep. Then the next morning she almost overslept!

She and Mrs. Wood went rushing out to catch a cab. They had to go from Chicago way out to Dyche Stadium in Evanston. By the time they found a cab it was late.

"Golly," said Babe, as they rode along, "I'd better get into my track clothes now. I won't have time if I wait till we get to the stadium."

"All right," said Mrs. Wood. "Here, I'll hold this blanket up. You can get behind it to change." Babe did. It turned out to be a good thing that she did. They reached Dyche Stadium just as the ceremonies were beginning.

"I hope all this confusion hasn't upset you, Babe," said Mrs. Wood.

"No, Mrs. Wood, it hasn't," said Babe. "I feel fine. In fact I feel wonderful! I guess I better run on ahead—it sounds like they're getting ready to start." Babe dashed forward.

A few minutes later she was waiting with the other contestants. There were over 200 girls entering the competition. They all stood near the side of the track.

The announcer started making the introductions. "The Illinois Women's Athtletic Club," boomed the loud speaker. Twenty-two young women trotted out on the field. As each team was announced, its members ran out. Usually there were twelve or fifteen girls on each team.

Then it was Babe's turn. "The Golden Cyclones of the Employers Casualty Company!" said the announcer. A lone figure raced out on the field. The crowd roared with approval.

Babe waved her arms and grinned. She could tell they were delighted with the idea of a one-girl team. Babe was delighted, too. "I guess I just naturally love an audience!" she thought to herself.

There were ten individual track and field events. Babe entered eight of them. She missed qualifying for the finals in the 100-meter dash, but she placed in every other event.

It seemed that Babe was all over the field. One

minute she was racing in the hurdles. The next minute she was taking her turn in the baseball throw. Then the voice came over the loud speaker to call her over to take one of her broad jumps. She had three busy hours.

Babe was very pleased when she came in fourth in the discus throw. "Because that's certainly no specialty of mine, goodness knows!"

Then she got ready to put the shot. "Well," said Babe to herself, "I'd better keep my fingers crossed on this one." Shot-putting wasn't a specialty of hers, either.

Babe took the heavy metal shot. She ran forward. Then she heaved the shot with all her strength. "Good throw, Babe," cried one of the bystanders.

The officials measured the throw. A few minutes later there was an announcement. "The Employers Casualty Company Team wins first place in the shot put. The distance was thirty-nine feet, six and one-fourth inches." Babe grinned delightedly. She was sure she could win some of the other events, but this win came as a pleasant surprise!

Some of the A.A.U. events were also Olympic trials. And in three of them Babe not only won —she broke the world's record! Twice the loud speaked boomed: "A new world's record has been set by Mildred Didrikson, Employers Casualty Company."

"Golly," said one of the spectators. "She's broken the world's record in the javelin *and* the eighty-meter hurdles!"

The man next to him looked at his program. "And not only that," he said. "The person who held the old world's record in both these events was also Mildred Didrikson!"

There was still the high jump. Soon all but two contestants were eliminated. Babe and another girl, Jean Shiley, were left. The announcer

said, "The bar is being moved up to five feet, three and three-sixteenth inches. This is one-sixteenth inch above the world's record. Miss Didrikson and Miss Shiley will try their jumps at that level."

First came Jean Shiley. She leaped over. Then Babe got ready. She jumped. She made it, too! The officials moved the bar up another fraction of an inch.

Jean Shiley tried it. She couldn't make it. Then Babe tried. She put her heart into it, but she couldn't quite get over it. The judges talked it over. Finally they announced, "This will be ruled a tie. Miss Didrikson and Miss Shiley will share first place."

Then the officials began to add up the points for the whole afternoon. The huge crowd buzzed with excitement. Then a hush settled over them.

The announcer walked up to the microphone. "Ladies and Gentlemen!" he said. The winner of the National A.A.U. Women's Track and Field Championship is—the Employers Casualty Company of Dallas, Texas!"

The crowd roared. Babe ran out to the platform to accept her trophy. The crowd stood up and cheered. Babe grinned from ear to ear.

Finally the cheering died down. The announcer was able to go on. "As the 'team' for the Employers Casualty Company, Miss Didrickson entered eight events. In seven of these she placed. In six of the eight she won first place! Miss Didrikson scored a total of thirty points."

The crowd broke into cheers again. Once more the announcer had to wait. Then he went on: "The second-place winner, with twenty-two points, is the Illinois Women's Athletic Club." That was the team with twenty-two girls! Babe couldn't help grinning even wider. By herself she had scored eight points more than the whole twenty-two put together!

Soon all the announcements were over. Babe went to look for Mrs. Wood. Mrs. Wood saw her and came running up to meet her.

"Oh, Babe!" she exclaimed. "You really did it! You won the national championship all by yourself!"

The next day Mrs. Wood got on a train for Dallas. She had all Babe's trophies. She was taking them home for her. "Good luck in Los Angeles, Babe," said Mrs. Wood. "I hope you'll bring home more trophies."

Babe caught the train to Los Angeles. Her victory in Chicago had won her a place on the Olympic Team as well as the national championship. Now she and the other girls were going to Los Angeles to train before the Olympics began.

The train started. Babe felt a little thrill of excitement as she settled down in her seat. Her dream was coming true. She was on her way to the Olympics!

The Olympics at Last

Some of the people riding on the train to Los Angeles with Babe probably told their friends about the trip later. Before it was over, everyone on the train knew Babe. They may not have known her name or anything about her. But before the train got to Los Angeles they certainly knew her by sight!

Babe was the only person who trained for the Olympics during the trip. Every day she worked out. She did exercises in the aisle. She ran the full length of the train.

Passengers looked up in surprise as she came trotting down the aisle. After awhile it got to be a sort of joke with them. "She's coming again!" they would call to each other.

Babe just grinned and kept right on practicing. She had been getting ready for the Olympics for almost four years. She certainly wasn't going to get out of condition now!

Soon Babe arrived in Los Angeles. She and the other girls on the Olympic Track and Field Team started practicing every day. The coach for that part of the Olympic Team was Mr. George Vreeland. Babe and Mr. Vreeland didn't get along too well.

"Miss Didrikson," said Mr. Vreeland, "I'm afraid there are quite a few changes you need to make. Your style in several of the events could be improved. You'll have to work pretty hard to get all the faults corrected before the Olympic Games start."

Babe got ready to say something. Mr. Vreeland went on. "For instance," he said, "in hurdling. You hold your front leg unusually high. In the correct position for going over the hurdle the front leg is straight out. And in the javelin——"

Babe interrupted. "Mr. Vreeland," she said firmly, "I'm sorry, but I'm not going to change my style in anything. I learned how to hurdle by jumping hedges. They were about two feet wide. I had to hold my front leg up high. If I hadn't, I'd have really got scratched. That's the natural way for me to hurdle now.

"I've had two coaches, Coach Lil Dimmitt and Colonel M. J. McCombs. They have told me to do things the way that comes natural. And that's what I am going to do!"

Mr. Vreeland looked at Babe. "Well," he said slowly, "I'm here to coach, Miss Didrikson. And I do think I could help you improve your form in several events.

"However, I must say that you are loyal to

your coaches. I can't help but admire that." He held out his hand. Babe shook it. "And I surely hope all three of you are right!" he said.

Finally the day came when Babe could show whether she was right. On Monday, August first, the 1932 Olympics began. For the opening parade Babe wore silk stockings for the first time in her life. She stood in the long line of American athletes. "This is it!" she thought to herself. "This is really it! I'm actually in the Olympics!" She felt her arms get goose pimply.

Late that afternoon Babe got ready for her first event. It was throwing the javelin. She looked down the field. "What's that little flag for?" she asked one of the other girls.

"That's to mark the distance of the Olympic record. A German girl was the one to set the record. That's why it's a German flag."

"Well, we'll see if we can make it an American flag," said Babe. She already held the world's record in the javelin throw. The Olympic record wasn't as far.

"If I aim just above that flag," thought Babe, "it should be about right." She got ready. The evening was cool. She hadn't had much chance to warm up. When she got ready to throw the javelin, her hand slipped.

Usually a javelin flies in an arc. This one didn't. It flew perfectly straight. Someone said it looked like a catcher's throw to second base. It flew about fourteen feet past the German flag!

The crowd cheered! Everyone knew instantly that Babe had set a new record. It proved to be both a new Olympic and a new world's record. That was Babe's first Olympic gold medal.

On Wednesday Babe got ready to run in the eighty-meter hurdles. "This is a record I'm going to break," she said confidently. The people who heard her smiled a little. But she was right!

In the early race, Babe both won and beat her

old world's record. The record had been 11.9 seconds. Now she made it 11.8.

The finals of the eighty-meter hurdles came the next day. "Think you can equal your yesterday's record, Babe?" someone asked.

"I'll do better than that," said Babe with a grin. "I'll set a new record." She got all ready. Then, just before the gun was fired, she started.

The official called everybody back. "Miss Didrikson," he said, "You are charged with one false start. You realize that if you jump the gun again, you will not be allowed to race. Do you understand this?"

"Yes, sir," answered Babe.

"All right," said the official. "Back to your places. We will try again."

Babe was tense. The shot rang out. Babe was determined not to jump the gun this time. She waited until she was sure everybody else had begun. Then she took off. And how she took off!

She soared over those hurdles. Over, over, over—how she flew! She was sure she was winning. Then, suddenly, Babe realized she wasn't alone. Miss Hall was right beside her!

"By golly," thought Babe. "Nobody's ever been this close before! We're neck and neck. I'd better really get going!" She ran harder.

There was the last hurdle and then—the ribbon. Would it still be unbroken when she got there? Babe shivered a little with excitement and worry as she touched the ribbon. It was still tight! She felt it break as she ran across the line.

Hooray! Once more the cheers rose from a thousand throats. Babe had done it again. Another first and another new world's record! She had run the eighty-meter hurdles in 11.7 seconds.

Babe had entered three Olympic events. That was all she was allowed to take part in. She had already won first place in two of them. Now she was ready for the third. It was the high jump.

Once again it turned out to be a contest between Babe and Jean Shiley. It had been that way in the National A.A.U. Meet.

There was an announcement. "The world's record in the Women's High Jump is five feet, three and one-eighth inches. The cross bar will be placed at five feet, five inches for this jump."

The crowd buzzed. They all knew that Babe had already broken world's records in her other two events. If she could make this jump, she would have broken records in all three!

Babe watched Jean Shiley get ready for her jump. Over she went. The crowd yelled. Babe got ready. She raced forward. Over *she* went! The crowd cheered again. Now Babe had broken the record in all three of her events!

She and Jean Shiley were still tied for first place, though. The loud speaker boomed out again. "The cross bar is now at five feet, five and one-half inches."

Jean Shiley took her jump. She made it! Still another world's record! Babe gritted her teeth. She raced forward. She jumped. She didn't make it. What a disappointment!

Everyone had two tries. "I've got one last chance!" she thought to herself. Once more she ran forward. This time she made it—over she sailed! Babe was a special favorite of the crowd. They cheered and cheered her.

The announcer spoke again. "The cross bar is being placed at five feet, five and three-fourths inches." Jean Shiley tried. She didn't make it.

"Now's my chance," thought Babe. She raced forward. She jumped. "This is what flying feels like!" she thought as she sailed over very easily.

She was so far above the cross bar that the crowd gasped. They had never seen a woman jump so high. Babe was three or four inches above the cross bar!

Babe was almost down. Then her foot hit the

side support. The cross bar fell! The crowd groaned. "Such a wonderful jump!" they told each other. "And now it won't count!"

They leaned forward to watch the next attempts. Neither Babe nor Jean could get over. The official announced: "The cross bar is being lowered to five feet, five and one-fourth inches. If both Miss Didrikson and Miss Shiley make this jump, it will be declared a first place tie."

A hush fell over the stadium. There was a

tense silence. Jean Shiley flew over. Then it was Babe's turn. She made it, too! "Well," she said to Jean Shiley, "looks like it's another twin first."

"It's getting to be a habit," Jean said.

Just then there was an announcement. "The judges have disqualified Miss Didrikson's jump. Miss Shiley wins first place."

Babe raced over to the judges' stand. "What happened?" she demanded. "What was wrong with that jump?"

The chief judge spoke. "You dived over. This western roll is new. It hasn't been seen very much. But you know that your feet must go over the bar first."

"But my feet did go over first!" insisted Babe. "I jumped just exactly like I've been jumping all afternoon."

"I'm sorry," said the judge. "That may be true. But if it is, we just didn't see it earlier. That last jump is definitely disqualified." He turned away.

Babe was bitterly disappointed. In a few minutes a crowd of sports writers came up to her. The most famous of the group was Grantland Rice. He had been writing a lot about Babe in the A.A.U. Meet and the Olympics.

"That's too bad, Babe," he said. "I think the judges were mistaken. But remember this: Most athletes would be walking on top of the world to get one Olympic gold medal. And you've got two gold ones and one silver!"

The Champion Comes Home

BABE LOOKED out the window. "Boy!" she said. "Things really look different from up here. I can hardly wait to tell Momma and Poppa what it feels like to fly. I'm the only person they know who's ever been in an airplane."

The girl beside her nodded. "I know. Here you are, not only coming back from the Olympics but coming back in a real airplane. And besides that, Dallas and Beaumont are having special 'Babe Didrikson Days' and everything. It really is exciting!"

"And this is going to be just about the most exciting part of all," said Babe. "I'll be seeing

Momma and Poppa in a few minutes now, and I can't wait. The man said we should be getting to Beaumont soon. Say, I think we're starting down now."

They were, too, for the plane was circling lower and lower. "Gee whiz, look at all the people!" cried Babe. "It looks like the whole town's at the airport." She leaned over as far as her seat belt would allow. Presently she said, "That looks like it might be—it is! It's Lillie, and there are Momma and Poppa right next to her!" Babe fairly bounced with excitement.

"Good heavens, Babe!" laughed the other girl. "Don't forget to wait for the plane to land."

Babe laughed, too. "Oh, I'll wait all right," she said without turning from the window, "but I'll bet I'll be the first one out on the ground after we *do* land!"

And she was. The minute the plane door was opened, Babe went dashing down the steps. She threw her arms around her parents and hugged them both at once.

"Oh, my Babe," Mrs. Didrikson said, "we're so proud of you!"

"Hey, Momma, you're crying," said Babe, leaning back to look at her.

"I guess everybody's sort of laughing and crying at the same time," said Lillie. She came up to give Babe a hug, too.

"And in front of all of Beaumont, too," said Poppa with a smile.

Babe turned toward the crowd. "Hi, everybody!" she yelled.

"Hi, Babe!" the crowd yelled back. Then the officials saw that Babe had had time to greet her family. Now they came forward. "This is Mayor Fletcher, Babe," one of them said.

"Hi, Mayor Fletcher," Babe said. She and the Mayor shook hands.

"And this is Fire Chief O'Conor," said the

official. "You're going to ride with him. We thought that bright red car of his would be a good one to lead the parade."

Babe shook hands with Chief O'Conor. "They'll be able to see us coming," she said with a grin. "Let's go!"

Chief O'Conor led the way to his car. Babe and Mr. and Mrs. Didrikson followed. Babe walked through the crowd laughing, talking, and shaking hands as she went.

When they got to the car, Babe stopped. "Boy, this really is something," she said. She ran her hand admiringly over the shiny surface of the car. "It's red all right!"

Chief O'Conor opened the door. "Please get in," he said. Mr. and Mrs. Didrikson got in the back seat and Babe got in front with the Chief. Slowly the long car began to move forward. The other cars in the parade moved, too. Babe turned around to watch.

"Just imagine us at the head of a parade, Momma," she said.

"I can hardly believe it," Mrs. Didrikson said.

"Momma's so happy to have you with both your feet on the ground again I doubt if she even knows we're *in* a parade," said Poppa. He patted his wife's hand.

"You really didn't need to worry, Momma," Babe said. "It wasn't as exciting as I thought it would be. I would have liked it lots better if we had done some rolls and dives and things. Now that would be fun!"

Mrs. Didrikson held up her hands. "My goodness, Babe, you sound just like you did when you had that circus in our backyard. I hope you aren't going to want to learn to drive an airplane!"

"You'd better start looking out the window now, Babe," said Chief O'Conor. "We're getting into town. Pretty soon there'll be people waiting to see you."

Babe turned. Soon they reached the downtown parade route. People were lined up on both sides of the street. They waved and yelled. Babe yelled and waved back. Some people even had signs saying, "Welcome home, Champ" or "Congratulations to the Beaumont Babe."

"I think I'll burst with pride, Ole," whispered Mrs. Didrikson.

"This is just the beginning, Momma," he whispered back.

And it *was* just the beginning. The parade of cars drove slowly to the Edson Hotel. Chief O'Conor's big red car stopped in front. Babe jumped out and the crowd lining the sidewalks burst into a cheer. Babe grinned and clasped her hands together. She held them above her head like a fighter who had just won a fight. Everyone laughed and clapped. Some people yelled, "Yea, Champ!" and "That's our Babe!"

By this time the Mayor and other officials had

joined Babe and they all went into the hotel. When they sat down to eat lunch in the dining room Babe suddenly realized she was hungry. She had completely forgotten about food. "It's chicken, too," she said as she looked at her plate. "One of my favorite foods." She began to eat.

"Just look at all the people, Poppa," said Mrs. Didrikson. She was so busy looking at the huge crowd attending the luncheon that she hadn't even touched her plate.

"Yes, and all here to honor our Babe," said Poppa. He couldn't help puffing out his chest a little.

One of the officials sitting near by heard him. "There were many more who wanted to come, Mr. Didrikson," he said. "We turned away hundreds who tried to buy tickets. I think everyone who ever went to school with Babe or saw her take part in any sport at all wanted to come today. All of Beaumont is proud of your girl."

"Thank you," said Poppa. He looked at his wife. They smiled at each other. They were mighty proud of their girl, too.

In a few weeks all the excitement was over. Babe had been honored in many ways, and now she was ready to go back to her old job with the Employers Casualty Company in Dallas. It had not occurred to her yet that she might earn her living in sports.

One morning, however, she received a letter from the Illinois Women's Athletic Club. She whistled when she read it, then went immediately to see the president of the Employers Casualty Company. "Mr. Mitchell," she said, "I have a letter here I think you ought to read. That Illinois Women's Athletic Club says it can get me a job in Chicago. I'd make $300 a month. I don't want to leave here, but that's more money than I've ever made in my whole life. I guess I'll almost have to go."

"You don't have to go, Babe," Mr. Mitchell said. "We'll give you three hundred dollars a month right here."

Babe smiled and leaned across the desk to shake Mr. Mitchell's hand. "Gee, thanks, Mr. Mitchell. I'm glad. I didn't want to leave."

When she left Mr. Mitchell's office, Babe was walking on air. "That extra money should start coming in time for Mother's Day," she thought. "Now I'll be able to buy something special for Momma." She grinned to herself. Buying something special for Momma and Poppa was the one thing she liked to do better than anything else in the world.

Babe went home for Mother's Day. She reached Beaumont late one Friday night. The next morning she was up early.

"My goodness, Babe," said Mrs. Didrikson, "I thought you would want to sleep this morning. You were up so late last night."

"I know," said Babe, "but I want to go downtown. I have some shopping to do. I'm going to look around, too. How about coming along with me?"

"All right," said Momma. "We'll have to go now, though. I want to get back by 10:30 to start dinner."

Off they went. Babe took her mother to several stores. Then she took her to the one she had really come to town to visit. It was an appliance store, which sold refrigerators and stoves.

"Oh, my!" said Mrs. Didrikson. "Look at all the beautiful stoves and ice boxes!"

"Those are mechanical refrigerators," Babe said. "You don't have to buy ice for them. They make their own ice."

Mrs. Didrikson touched the smooth white sides of one of the refrigerators. "To look so pretty and to work so well, too!" she said.

Babe smiled. "Momma," she said, "if we were

millionaires and you could have anything you wanted in this whole store, which ones would you choose?"

Momma put her finger on her chin. She looked everything over very carefully. "Well," she said at last, "if I were picking out a stove for the millionaire Didriksons, I'd take this one." She pointed to a stove. "And I'd take this ice box."

Babe laughed. "I'll say one thing for you, Momma. You picked the two most expensive ones in the whole place!"

Mrs. Didrikson laughed, too. "We millionaires never worry about little things like that, you know." Then she took Babe's arm and they went home.

Right after dinner Babe said, "I'm going out for a while, Momma. I'll be home before supper." She hurried back to the appliance store.

"I want to buy that stove and refrigerator my mother picked out this morning," she told the salesman who had waited on them earlier. "There's one thing, though. I don't have enough money to pay for them all at once. I could make a down payment. Then you could let me have the rest on credit. Would you do that?" At that time people did not buy things on credit much. It was not the usual way of doing business.

The salesman thought a while. Then he said, "Why don't you just come back later? You could wait until you have the money to pay for them. I'd be glad to order you another stove and refrigerator just like these if they're sold before you're ready."

"Thank you," Babe said, "but I have to have them right away—tomorrow, in fact. I want to give them to Momma for a Mother's Day present. Won't you *please* let me have them on credit?"

The salesman looked at Babe's face. He could tell how much she wanted the appliances. "Well," he said, "I'll be here for a while tomorrow. Come down to the store in the morning. We'll work something out."

"Thank you!" said Babe. She shook his hand so hard he was afraid it might come off! "I'll see you tomorrow!"

The next morning Babe hurried down to the store. The salesman was waiting. Babe signed papers agreeing to buy the appliances on credit. "We have a sort of a problem, Miss Didrikson," said the salesman. "Since this is Sunday, we have only two men here to make deliveries. I'm not sure they'll be able to handle your things."

"That's all right," said Babe. "I'll ride in the truck with them to help out. I want to call home before we start, though." In a few moments she was talking to Lillie on the telephone. "Lillie," she said, "I want you to get Momma out of the house for a while. I'll tell you when to bring her back. We should be there in about twenty minutes, so have her next door by then."

"Okay, Babe," said Lillie. "I'll suggest it right now." Lillie was as good as her word. When the delivery truck drove up, Mrs. Didrikson and Lillie were next door.

"Now we'll have to hurry," said Babe. She helped the men get the heavy stove and refrigerator off the truck and into the house. While the men were connecting the new appliances, Babe was busy, too. Mrs. Didrikson had dinner cooking on her old stove. Babe moved everything off the old stove and onto the new. Then she put the things from the old ice box into the new refrigerator. "Boy, will Momma be surprised!" thought Babe. She smiled just thinking about it.

"Everything's all hooked up and ready to go, ma'am," said one of the delivery men.

"Fine," said Babe. "Thanks a lot. Now if you'll just drive your truck away so Momma won't see it, I'll go and get her." The men drove away

and Babe hurried outside to the yard. She cupped her hands to her mouth. "Hey, Lillie!" she called. "I'm home!"

In a few moments Lillie and Mrs. Didrikson came back from next door. "Isn't is almost time for dinner, Momma?" asked Babe. "I'm starved."

"I never saw you when you weren't, young lady," said her mother. "I'm going to the kitchen right now to check on things."

Mrs. Didrikson started toward the stove. Then she saw that it wasn't her old stove standing there. It was the wonderful new stove she had seen in the store. She could hardly believe it. Then, before she could say anything about that, she saw the new refrigerator. It was just too much! She sat down in the nearest chair and burst into tears.

Babe ran over to her. "How do you like your Mother's Day present, Momma?" she asked, hugging her. "How do you like it?"

"Oh, Babe!" said Mrs. Didrikson. She threw her arms around her daughter's neck. "My Babe! My Babe! You did all this!" She still couldn't quite believe that it was really happening.

"You know, Momma," said Babe a little later, "even if I were to win every single gold medal in the Olympics I don't think anything could ever make me happier than this."

Golf Comes to the Fore

"MOMMA, POPPA," said Babe, "how would you like to have a vacation in California? I've been saving my money this whole year since the Olympics. I've decided I'm going to California to learn how to play golf. The three of us will have a summer out there."

"You're going to learn to play golf, Babe?" asked her father.

"Yes, Poppa," she answered. "I've decided that's the game for me. You remember my telling you about that golf game I played right after the Olympics? The one I played with Grantland Rice and the other sports writers?"

"Sure, I remember," said Poppa. He grinned. "That was quite a game." It had been, too. Mr. Rice and the others had wanted to see how well Babe would do in a game she hadn't really played or worked at.

"You haven't played much golf, have you?" asked Mr. Rice.

"No, not much," Babe had answered. "I played a little in high school. Once I hit a few balls on a driving range with Colonel McCombs. That's about all, though."

The next day, when they got ready to play, Mr. Rice said, "Okay, Babe, ladies first. You start."

Babe drove the ball far down the fairway.

"Wow!" said Mr. Rice. All the men were amazed.

"Two hundred and forty yards if it's an inch!" they shouted. And Babe's drive was the longest. Not one of the four men hit the ball that far.

That was the first of many famous golf games for Babe. But she wasn't ready for them then. She and Mr. and Mrs. Didrikson went to California the summer of 1933. Momma and Poppa had their vacation. Babe studied golf.

She met a golf teacher named Stan Kertes. Golf lessons were very expensive. But Mr. Kertes thought Babe was so good he taught her free. Babe worked with him every day.

Finally the money ran out. Babe and Mr. and Mrs. Didrikson went back to Texas. Babe went to work for the Employers Casualty Company again. But she kept working at her golf. She was sure now she wanted to make golf her main sport for life.

At the end of 1934 Babe decided to enter her first golf tournament. It was in Fort Worth. "I might as well see what I've learned," she said to herself. In the qualifying round she shot seventy-seven. That won her a medal for the best score.

"Maybe I'll try for the state tournament now," she said. The Texas State Women's Golf championship was to be held in the spring of 1935. Babe started getting ready. She practiced for it just as she always had practiced for any sport.

Every free moment she worked, worked, worked. Often her hands were blistered. She put tape on them and went right on practicing. And at night she studied the golf rules.

After three months of hard training, Babe entered the tournament. She played with all her might, just as she had always done everything. Thirty-two women qualified. Finally only Babe and one other person were left.

The other person was Peggy Chandler. She had been in the finals for the past three years. She and Babe seesawed back and forth. First one would be ahead, then the other.

There was one time when Babe needed all her confidence. Her ball stopped in a rut. "Boy, look at that," said one person watching. "Her ball is half covered with water."

"And it is so far from the green," said another. "She needs to tie Peggy Chandler on this hole. To do that she will have to get the ball in the cup in three strokes. I don't think she can do it."

Babe looked at the ball carefully. She thought about everything her golf teachers had told her. Then she hit the ball with all her might. The ball shot into the air. It sailed toward the green.

Suddenly Babe heard a roar from the crowd around the green. The ball had gone right into the cup! Everyone cheered. When the finals were over, Babe had won by two holes.

That was the first of Babe's big tournaments. She went on to play many of them. She played both as an amateur and as a professional. She won tournament after tournament.

One of the golf tournaments Babe remembered best was the 1938 Los Angeles Open. It was mostly a men's tournament, but women could play, too.

Babe entered. Her partners were a minister and a wrestler. The minister, Pardee Erdman, was to become a friend. The wrestler, George Zaharias, was to become her husband!

Babe said later, "I knew almost at once that this was *it!*" Evidently George felt the same way. Less than six months later they were engaged. They were married that same year.

People noticed a big change in Babe about this time. She had never been much interested in clothes before. She had worn her hair in a boyish-looking style and had worn no makeup.

Now she began to want to look more like a girl. She curled her hair. She wore jewelry and high-heeled shoes. She wore lipstick. It was amazing how different she looked. Her friends started saying, "Why, Babe, how pretty you look!"

George kept on wrestling. Babe kept on playing golf. They tried to arrange their schedules so they could be together as much as possible.

In 1946 Babe won her first national golf championship. She had won three tournaments straight before that one. Then, right after the National Women's Amateur championship, she won another tournament. That made five.

"I'm coming home to rest awhile, George," she said. "Now that we've got our first home I want to be there to enjoy it. My roses need me."

"I know, Honey," said George. "But you mustn't stop now. Keep on with this winning streak. You'll make golf history."

"Well, all right," said Babe. "I surely wish you could come, too, though," she added.

Babe went on with her tournaments. She entered one after another. She played in Florida, Georgia, North Carolina, and Washington. She kept winning and winning. Soon she had a streak of fifteen victories.

"The next thing for you to do is to win the British Women's Amateur Golf Tournament," said George.

"I don't know," said Babe. "It's too far away from home—and you."

"Maybe I can try to come over later," said George. "Anyway, you can't miss this. This is just what you need. It will add a really big one to your streak of wins."

"Well, I guess I'll let you persuade me," said Babe, smiling. And she was never sorry she did. She had a wonderful time in Scotland. The Scottish crowds following the tournament soon became her fans.

"I guess I still love an audience," Babe said with a grin. They loved her, too. And she won the tournament! "And, of course, I still love to win!" she said. When Babe's winning streak was finally broken, she had won seventeen tournaments straight!

Much as she had enjoyed Scotland, Babe was glad to start home. "I can hardly wait to get home," she said. "Back to my roses, back to my house, back to George!"

The trip home was wonderful. The Scottish people filled her train compartment with flowers. Crowds gathered at the station to sing "Auld Lang Syne" as she left.

Babe sailed home on the "Queen Elizabeth." One day she heard a loud commotion. "I wonder what that is," she thought. "We can't be in New York. We're supposed to get there in about three hours."

It was a boat. "It's loaded down with newsreel cameramen and reporters, Mrs. Zaharias," said one of the crew members. "They are all coming out to take pictures of you." Babe went to the deck rail.

She kept looking at the boat. "That's not all it's loaded with," she said. She grinned from ear to ear. "You see that big fellow in the white shirt standing in the front? That's my husband!"

Babe and George stayed in New York a few days. Once again Babe was a major celebrity. Her phone was ringing all the time. Reporters kept coming to talk to her and write stories about her. Photographers kept coming to take her picture.

Then it was time to go home to Denver. That's where she and George lived. And Denver was waiting. The townspeople felt Babe belonged to them now. They were very proud of her.

The Mayor of Denver and the Governor of Colorado welcomed her. "We have a big parade planned in your honor, Mrs. Zaharias," said an official. "You see, there's a float for each of the sports you're famous for."

Babe looked as she walked past the floats. "I see!" she said. "Here's basketball, hurdling, throwing the javelin, baseball——"

"And lots of others, too," said the official. "And here's the last float. We'd like for you to sit on it."

"Just look at all the roses!" cried Babe. "The float's loaded with them!" She smiled. "I don't know if there'll even be room for me," she said.

The official smiled, too. "They're your favorite flower, aren't they?"

"Yes, indeed," said Babe. "I just love roses."

A few minutes later Babe was riding in the parade. She waved and threw roses to the crowd. She had a wonderful time.

At the end of the parade there was a ceremony. The speaker said, "I'm going to read a list given me by Tiny Scurlock, sports editor of the Beaumont *Journal*, Beaumont, Texas. About ten years ago, he asked a certain Beaumont athlete to name her sports. These are the things she listed:

Basketball	Baseball	Water Polo
Track	Bowling	Horseback Riding
Swimming	Skating	Canoeing

Diving	Boxing	Archery
Hockey	Wrestling	Croquet
Polo	Shooting	Dominoes
Tennis	Surf Boating	Checkers
Golf	Ice Skating	

The crowd laughed as he read the last two. Babe grinned. The speaker continued. "Then Mr. Scurlock asked this young athlete, 'What have you found the hardest sport to master? Why?'

"And do you know what the answer was? 'There's no hard sport as far as I'm concerned—and that's the truth!' And the remarkable thing is," said the speaker, "evidently that really is the truth! And here's the person who made that list, ladies and gentlemen, the greatest woman athlete of this—or perhaps any—century, Mrs. Babe Didrikson Zaharias!"

ACKNOWLEDGEMENTS

We the authors, Lena de Grummond and Lynne de Grummond Delaune, should like to express our deep appreciation to the following:

Mrs. William Scurlock who gave us free access to the files of her late husband, William "Tiny" Scurlock, of the Beaumont *Journal*, and who gave us other help and encouragement.

Mr. J. W. Irvine, who first suggested that we write a childhood biography of Babe Didrikson Zaharias, and who interviewed Mr. Lil Dimmitt for us.

Mrs. Lillie Didrickson Grimes, who gave us personal and family information on her sister.

Mr. and Mrs. Ernest Goodman, Mr. Bob Aldridge, Mr. C. L. Pierce, Miss Pearl Andrus, Mr. and Mrs. Tony Montalbano, and others of Beaumont who furnished us information.

Mrs. Virgil Anzalone of Independence, La., who gave able assistance in the recording of interviews with relatives, friends, and neighbors of Babe.

We have tried to present a true picture of the childhood of this famous athlete, reconstructing actual events in some cases and probable ones, based on general facts, in others.

In several instances our research turned up information different from that given in Mrs. Zaharias's autobiography* (the date of her birth, for example). When this happened, we used the information gleaned from our careful research and checked against official and contemporary documents.

We should also like to express our appreciation to Lt. Col. Richard K. Delaune, Richie, Linden, and especially Jonathan, without whose cooperation this book could not have been written.

*Babe Didrikson Zaharias, as told to Harry Paxton, *This Life I've Led, My Autobiography*, A. S. Barnes & Co., Inc., New York, 1955.

More About This Book

WHEN BABE DIDRIKSON LIVED

1913 "BABE," MILDRED ELLA DIDRIKSON WAS BORN IN PORT ARTHUR, TEXAS, JUNE 26.

There were forty-eight states in the Union.

Woodrow Wilson was President.

The population of the country was about 102,095,000.

1916–1929 BABE LIVED IN BEAUMONT, TEXAS, AND WON MANY SPORTS EVENTS.

The United States entered World War 1, 1917.

The Armistice was signed, ending World War I, 1918.

Regular radio broadcasts were begun, 1920.

Women in the United States received the right to vote, 1920.

The first full-length talking motion picture was made, 1927.

Charles A. Lindbergh flew a small airplane across the Atlantic Ocean, 1927.

1929–1932 BABE WORKED IN DALLAS, TEXAS, AND WON NATIONAL RECORDS IN BASKETBALL.

Richard E. Byrd flew over the South Pole, 1929.

Alexander Fleming discovered penicillin, 1929.

Stock market prices crashed and a severe business depression followed, 1929.

1932–1935 BABE WON TWO GOLD MEDALS IN THE OLYMPICS AND CONTINUED TO WORK IN DALLAS.

Amelia Earhart flew a small airplane across the Atlantic Ocean, 1932.

The Tennessee Valley Act was passed, establishing T.V.A., 1933.

Social Security with old age benefits was founded, 1935.

1935–1955 BABE BECAME A GOLFER AND SET A RECORD FOR WINNING GOLF TOURNAMENTS.

World War II was fought, 1939-1945.

The first atomic bomb was exploded in a test at Alamogordo, New Mexico, 1945.

The United Nations Charter was adopted, 1945.

The Korean War was fought, 1950-1953.

1956 BABE, NOW MRS. GEORGE ZAHARIAS, DIED.

There were forty-eight states in the Union.

Dwight D. Eisenhower was President.

The population of the country was about 167,270,000.

DO YOU REMEMBER?

1. How does the beginning of the story show that Babe was a lively girl?
2. Why did the boys on both baseball teams want Babe to play with them?
3. What kind of tournament did Babe win when she was in the second grade at school?
4. What kind of show did the Didrikson children put on in the back yard?
5. How did she help the neighborhood team win a football game?
6. How did she and her sister prepare for the Olympics in 1932?
7. How did she become named "all-city, all-state" in basketball in Texas?

8. How did she get an opportunity to play basketball in Dallas, Texas?
9. How did she win four events in a track meet which was held in Dallas?
10. How did she win the National A.A.U. Women's Track and Field Championship?
11. What events did she win in the 1932 Olympics in Los Angeles?
12. What did she do for her mother once when she went home for Mother's Day?
13. How did she happen to meet George Zaharias, who later became her husband?
14. What great success did she have in winning golf tournaments both here and abroad?

IT'S FUN TO LOOK UP THESE THINGS

1. Where is Beaumont, Texas, in which Babe Didrikson lived as a girl?
2. How are state high school basketball tournaments usually conducted?
3. What sports are ordinarily included in track and field events?

4. What is the Amateur Athletic Union (A.A.U.) in which Babe Didrikson participated?
5. What are the Olympic Games, and where were they first held?
6. Who are some of the most famous golfers in our country today?

INTERESTING THINGS YOU CAN DO

1. Make a list of all the games and sports that Babe Didrikson took part in.
2. Collect pictures of Babe participating in different games and sports to show to the class or to display on the bulletin board.
3. Find out what noted athletes in this country have recently won honors in different events at the Olympic Games.
4. Prepare a short report explaining how to play the game, basketball.
5. Explain what a tournament is and how it differs from a game.
6. Tell which game or sport you like best, and explain why you like it.

OTHER BOOKS YOU MAY ENJOY READING

Everygirls Sports Stories, A. L. Furman, ed. Lantern.

Jim Thorpe: Indian Athlete, Guernsey Van Riper, Jr. Trade and School Editions, Bobbs-Merrill.

Junior Illustrated Encyclopedia of Sports, Herbert Kam and Willard Mullin. Bobbs-Merrill.

Lou Gehrig: Boy of the Sandlots, Guernsey Van Riper, Jr. Trade and School Editions, Bobbs-Merrill.

Story of Sports, Frank Jupo. Dodd, Mead.

This Life I've Led, Babe Didrikson Zaharias. A. S. Barnes.

INTERESTING WORDS IN THIS BOOK

acrobat (ăk′rō băt) : person trained to do gymnastics, as walking a rope, swinging on a trapeze, or turning somersaults

amateur (ăm′*ȧ* tûr) : person who takes part in a game or sport for pleasure, not for money

annual (ăn′ū *ă*l) : publication put out once a year

aquaplane (ăk′w*ȧ* plān′) : wide board on which a person may ride behind a speedboat

barker (bär′kẽr): person who speaks to crowds at a show to persuade them to enter

chinaberry (chī′nȧ bẽr′ĭ): tree that grows in the southern part of the United States

compartment (kŏm pärt′mĕnt): small room for traveling in a railroad car

competition (kŏm′pė tĭsh′ŭn): act of trying to win a game or contest against others

concentrating (kŏn′sĕn trāt ĭng): centering attention on something

cross bar (krôs′bär′): long pole or rod over which a high jumper must jump

decision (dė sĭzh′ŭn): conclusion

discus (dĭs′kŭs): heavy circular plate that athletes throw as a test of strength and skill

gesture (jĕs′tůr): movement of a part of the body to supplement or take the place of words

hurdle (hûr′d'l): special frame which runners must jump over in certain races

impressive (ĭm prĕs′ĭv): having the power to give people favorable feelings

javelin (jăv′lĭn): long, slender wooden spear thrown in track and field contests

malt (môlt): malted milk made at a soda fountain

meter (mē′tẽr): unit of measurement equal to about thirty-nine inches

professional (prȯ fĕsh′ŭn ăl): person who specializes in certain games or sports and takes part for money

rhythm (rĭth'm): motion taking place again and again in a regular manner

reporter (rē pōr′tẽr): person who writes new articles about different things that happen

schedules (skĕd′ūlz): list of events and the dates on which they will occur

sickle (sĭk′'l): sharp tool with a handle and curved blade, used for cutting

sleight-of-hand (slīt ŭv hănd): trick of making things appear or disappear through skillful words and use of the hands

slide rule: kind of ruler used to work problems in mathematics

stadium (stā′dĭ ŭm): large field surrounded by seats, used for athletic contests

stilts (stĭlts): tall poles with steps for the feet, used in walking to make a person appear unusually tall

varsity (vär′sĭ tĭ): refers to the regular team that represents a school in any sport

Childhood
OF FAMOUS AMERICANS

COLONIAL DAYS

JAMES OGLETHORPE, *Parks*
MYLES STANDISH, *Stevenson*
PETER STUYVESANT, *Widdemer*
POCAHONTAS, *Seymour*
SQUANTO, *Stevenson*
VIRGINIA DARE, *Stevenson*
WILLIAM BRADFORD, *Smith*
WILLIAM PENN, *Mason*

STRUGGLE for INDEPENDENCE

ANTHONY WAYNE, *Stevenson*
BEN FRANKLIN, *Stevenson*
BETSY ROSS, *Weil*
DAN MORGAN, *Bryant*
ETHAN ALLEN, *Winders*
FRANCIS MARION, *Steele*
GEORGE ROGERS CLARK, *Wilkie*
GEORGE WASHINGTON, *Stevenson*
ISRAEL PUTNAM, *Stevenson*
JOHN PAUL JONES, *Snow*
MARTHA WASHINGTON, *Wagoner*
MOLLY PITCHER, *Stevenson*
NATHAN HALE, *Stevenson*
NATHANAEL GREENE, *Peckham*
PATRICK HENRY, *Barton*
PAUL REVERE, *Stevenson*
TOM JEFFERSON, *Monsell*

EARLY NATIONAL GROWTH

ABIGAIL ADAMS, *Wagoner*
ALEC HAMILTON, *Higgins*
ANDY JACKSON, *Stevenson*
DAN WEBSTER, *Smith*
DEWITT CLINTON, *Widdemer*
DOLLY MADISON, *Monsell*
ELIAS HOWE, *Corcoran*
ELI WHITNEY, *Snow*
FRANCIS SCOTT KEY, *Stevenson*
HENRY CLAY, *Monsell*
JAMES FENIMORE COOPER, *Winders*
JAMES MONROE, *Widdemer*
JOHN AUDUBON, *Mason*
JOHN JACOB ASTOR, *Anderson*
JOHN MARSHALL, *Monsell*
JOHN QUINCY ADAMS, *Weil*
LUCRETIA MOTT, *Burnett*
MATTHEW CALBRAITH PERRY, *Scharbach*
NANCY HANKS, *Stevenson*
NOAH WEBSTER, *Higgins*
OLIVER HAZARD PERRY, *Long*
RACHAEL JACKSON, *Govan*
ROBERT FULTON, *Henry*
SAMUEL MORSE, *Snow*
SEQUOYAH, *Snow*
STEPHEN DECATUR, *Smith*
STEPHEN FOSTER, *Higgins*
WASHINGTON IRVING, *Widdemer*
ZACK TAYLOR, *Wilkie*

WESTWARD MOVEMENT

BRIGHAM YOUNG, *Jordan and Frisbee*
BUFFALO BILL, *Stevenson*
DANIEL BOONE, *Stevenson*
DAVY CROCKETT, *Parks*
JED SMITH, *Burt*
JESSIE FREMONT, *Wagoner*
JIM BOWIE, *Winders*